SIMPLE SECRETS OF
Happiness

SIMPLE SECRETS OF
Happiness

What Scientists Have Learned
and How You Can Use It

David Niven, Ph.D.

HarperSanFrancisco
A Division of HarperCollinsPublishers

Contents

Contents

Acknowledgments

I am grateful for the fine work of Gideon Weil and the staff at HarperSanFrancisco who have helped to make this book a better tool for its readers.

I also thank my agents, Maureen Lasher and Eric Lasher, whose interest and faith in this project were invaluable.

A Note to Readers

Each of the 100 entries presented here is based on the research conclusions of scientists studying happiness and life satisfaction. Each entry contains a key research finding, complemented by advice and an example that follow from the finding. The research conclusions presented in each entry are based on a meta-analysis of research on happiness, which means that each conclusion is derived from the work of multiple researchers studying the same topic. To enable the reader to find further information on each topic, a reference to a supporting study is included in each entry, and a bibliography of recent work on happiness has also been provided.

Introduction:
All I Can Do Is Point and Hope You Look

Harry Gilman has spent his career studying people, and he knows that often what many people want and need is right in front of their faces, if only they could see it.

"No one can snap their fingers and make someone happy. What you can do is help people to see what is useful for them to see. What you can do is point and hope they look."

Harry Gilman is a psychology professor. He could have carved a fine existence out of publishing academic research and lecturing on that research to his colleagues. But unlike many professors, Harry didn't see his job as publishing scientific papers for scientific readers. He said in a seminar one time, "What would be the point of finding out something and then never telling anyone who could really use the information? Why play 'I've got a secret' your entire life? Psychology professors who figure out a better way to think about life spend their careers sharing it with other professors."

One of the many things that made Harry an extraordinary teacher was that he cared. In his psychology seminars, he required every student to submit a notebook—a bound, marbleized notebook, to be exact—every week. In it we were told to write something, anything. What did we think about? What were our concerns? What were our hopes, fears? These were the questions the students returned to week after week.

We were so taken with the process that many of us shared our notebooks with one another. Max Leer, one of my classmates, almost always wrote about his relationship with his father, a man who never seemed satisfied with his life or with Max.

Harry would read our entries closely and comment on them. To Max, Harry wrote, "Max, for some people there are no victories, just alternate forms of losing."

That phrase never left me. It was a powerful way of sending home the point that Harry had been making in class: much in life is simply a matter of perspective. It's not inherently good or bad, a success or failure; it's how we choose to look at things that makes the difference.

"What do you make of life? That's the question," Harry said to the class. "Sugar, flour, and eggs—are they good or bad? You could make of them a cake, or you could just make a mess. But then that cake, or that mess—is it good or bad? Can you make it good? Of course. Can you make it bad? Certainly."

Another day, Harry impressed upon me and my classmates what he called the nearly boundless capacity of humans to ignore the long-term implications of their decisions while they focus on short-term effects. He spoke of the difference between an impartial, logical observer, who would always make long-term decisions, and the person who can't see beyond their immediate gratification. "A child will always reach for the lollipop; only the adult watching thinks tooth decay and lack of nutrition," Harry said. "We have to strive to be the adult watching above, not just living the moment, but seeing from outside ourselves what is happening, what should be happening, what things we are doing that will ultimately hurt us."

Harry's classes interested us, and Harry inspired us. With graduation fast approaching, our conversation often drifted to the subject of our futures and career choices. "What can you do with psychology?" Harry asked us rhetorically. "All we can do is give out the best answers we have. Then people have a chance to use them."

On graduation day, I went up to Harry to shake his hand. "I don't know how to thank you, Harry. You made me a better person."

"Thank you, David," Harry responded, "but I didn't make you a better person. All I can do is point and hope you look."

I offer you *The 100 Simple Secrets of Happy People* in that spirit—pointing to findings of psychological research on happy people, and hoping you will look.

What do happy people do differently than unhappy people? Psychology's best observations appear in academic journals like the *Journal of Personality and Social Psychology* and the *Journal of Applied Behavioral Science.* But you may not have access to these journals, and even if you did, you would find them written in scientific gobbledygook, not understandable English.

That's where *The 100 Simple Secrets of Happy People* comes in. After reviewing over a thousand studies written during the last decade exploring the characteristics and beliefs of happy people, I have taken the best, most practical advice from that body of research. Instead of using academic jargon, *The 100 Simple Secrets of Happy People* translates the conclusions of this research into simple, useful advice.

Each study on happiness has been boiled down to its core and then expressed in a way everyone will understand. With the scientific results of research as its foundation, *The 100 Simple Secrets of Happy People* offers 100 simple pieces of advice and examples of how people find happiness and stay happy.

The 100 Simple Secrets of Happy People is not just one person's intuition. Rather, it reflects the research conclusions of noted scientists studying the lives of regular people. My interpretation and translation of this research will help those who want to know more about the differences between happy and unhappy people. It will also help those who want to know what they can do to enjoy life more. I'm pointing now, and I hope you will look.

1

Your life has purpose and meaning.

You are not here just to fill space or to be a background character in someone else's movie.

Consider this: nothing would be the same if you did not exist. Every place you have ever been and everyone you have ever spoken to would be different without you.

We are all connected, and we are all affected by the decisions and even the existence of those around us.

Take the example of Peter, an attorney in Philadelphia, and his dog, Tucket. Tucket was very sick. Gradually he was becoming paralyzed by a tumor on his spinal cord.

Peter could not find a veterinary doctor who could save his dog. Desperate to find someone who could help, he turned to a pediatric neurosurgeon. The doctor agreed to try to help Tucket, and in return he asked Peter for a donation to the children's hospital he worked in.

Jerry has never met Peter or Tucket. Jerry is a blue-eyed, blond-haired, five-year-old boy who loves to eat mashed potatoes. Jerry also has tumors on his spine and in his brain.

With help from the donation Peter made to the hospital, Jerry underwent successful surgery performed by the doctor to remove the tumors.

Tucket's surgery was also a success.

☺   ☺   ☺

Studies of older Americans find that one of the best predictors of happiness is whether a person considers his or her life to have a purpose. Without a clearly defined purpose, seven in ten individuals feel unsettled about their lives; with a purpose, almost seven in ten feel satisfied.

Lepper 1996

2

Use a strategy for happiness.

We assume that happy and unhappy people are born that way. But both kinds of people do things that create and reinforce their moods. Happy people let themselves be happy. Unhappy people continue doing things that upset them.

What is the first sign of a healthy business? A healthy business plan. That is the argument of the Strategic Management Center, a business consulting firm. They believe every business must define its purpose and then create a strategy to accomplish that purpose.

This same approach can be used by people. Define what you want, then use a strategy to get it.

Ironically, children are better at this than adults. Small children know when being cranky will get them an ice cream cone. And they know when being too noisy will get them a cross reaction from their parents. Children understand that there are rules and predictable patterns to life, and they use a strategy to help them get what they want.

Living a happy life as an adult is like trying to get that ice cream cone as a child. You need to know what you want and use a strategy to get it. Think about what makes you happy and what makes you sad, and use this to help you get what you want.

Happy people do not experience one success after another and unhappy people, one failure after another. Instead, surveys show that happy and unhappy people tend to have had very similar life experiences. The difference is that the average unhappy person spends more than twice as much time thinking about unpleasant events in their lives, while happy people tend to seek and rely upon information that brightens their personal outlook.

Lyubomirsky 1994

3

You don't have to win every time.

Ultracompetitive people, who always need to win, end up enjoying things less. If they lose they are very disappointed, and if they win it's what they expected would happen anyway.

Richard Nixon was running for reelection as president in 1972. He directed his campaign staff to take all available measures to win as many votes as possible. Most famous, of course, were the break-ins they staged at Democratic Party headquarters in the Watergate building in order to plant bugging devices. But staff workers also engaged in an endless series of what Nixon himself labeled "dirty tricks." They would call up pizza parlors and order a hundred pizzas to be delivered to the office of an opposition candidate. They would hand out phony fliers telling people that an opponent's rally had been canceled. They would call meeting halls and cancel reservations opponents had made for events. Why did they do these things? Nixon was obsessed with winning—at all costs.

The great irony was that Nixon was winning anyway and didn't need any of these tricks. But his inability to deal with the possibility of losing caused him to pursue these extreme methods and ultimately cost him the prize that he had so desperately pursued.

Competitiveness can preclude life satisfaction because no accomplishment can prove sufficient, and failures are particularly devastating. Ultracompetitive people rate their successes with lower marks than some people rate their failures.

Thurman 1981

4

Your goals should be aligned with one another.

The four tires of your car have to be properly aligned; otherwise the left tires will be pointed in a different direction from the right tires and the car won't work. Goals are just like that. They all must be pointed in the same direction. If your goals conflict with one another, your life may not work.

Jorge Ramos was on the fast track in television news. He anchored a broadcast that could be seen in the U.S. and Latin America. He covered major political figures and jumped at the chance to cover wars—and risk his life—in the Middle East, Latin America, and Europe.

Ramos was doing exceptionally well by his own calculations, both professionally and economically. He wished to push his career even further. He wanted to "peer into the hearts of those that dominate the planet and be at the places where history changes."

But Ramos was also missing his family, all the time. When he was away from home, viewing a picture of his daughter could make him cry as he thought about the time apart, the distance, the danger that he had exposed himself to and the effect that could have on her.

Ramos eventually realized he could not keep his goal of being where the action was and being where he needed to be most—with his family.

In a long-term study of subjects over the course of more than a decade, life satisfaction was associated with the consistency of life goals. Goals regarding career, education, family, and geography were each important, and together add up to about 80 percent of satisfaction. These goals need to be consistent with one another to produce positive conclusions regarding goal achievement.

Wilson, Henry, and Peterson 1997

5

Choose your comparisons wisely.

Many of our feelings of satisfaction or dissatisfaction have their roots in how we compare ourselves to others. When we compare ourselves to those who have more, we feel bad. When we compare ourselves to those who have less, we feel grateful. Even though the truth is we have exactly the same life either way, our feelings about our life can vary tremendously based on who we compare ourselves with. Compare yourself with those examples that are meaningful but that make you feel comfortable with who you are and what you have.

Joe is the oldest of six brothers. The brothers range in age from twenty-one to forty-two. His family never had a lot of money, and the older brothers especially grew up in modest circumstances. When they finished high school, Joe and the two older brothers went to work. When the three younger brothers finished high school, however, they went to college. The older brothers feel like they missed out. Since financial aid wasn't as plentiful, they really didn't have a chance to get more education.

If they compare themselves to their younger brothers, Joe and the older brothers may feel disappointment and jealousy. They may ask, Why did they get opportunities I did not? But if they compare themselves to many of their friends—men their age, men who had similar opportunities—the brothers see that they have more than most of their friends in terms of job satisfaction and a fulfilling family life.

Of course, Joe would gain no advantage by depriving his younger siblings of their opportunities. But he still feels bad when he compares himself to them. The answer, then, is not to make that comparison. The younger brothers grew up two decades later, in a different world and in many respects in a different family. Instead of disappointing themselves by making this comparison, Joe and the older brothers can feel good about both their younger brothers and themselves when they make a more realistic comparison to those who faced the same challenges as they did.

A large group of students was given a word puzzle to solve. Researchers compared the satisfaction of students who finished the puzzle quickly or more slowly. Students who finished the puzzle quickly and compared themselves with the very fastest students came away feeling dissatisfied with themselves. Students who finished the puzzle more slowly but compared themselves with the slowest students came away feeling quite satisfied with themselves and tended to ignore the presence of the quick-finishing students.

Lyubomirsky and Ross 1997

6

Cultivate friendships.

Rekindle past relationships, and take advantage of opportunities at work or among your neighbors to expand your friendship base. People need to feel that they are a part of something bigger, that they care about others and are cared about by others in return.

☺　☺　☺

Andy didn't really know his neighbors. He would wave if he saw them in the yard, but mainly what he saw were tall fences and closed doors.

Andy had bought himself a computer a few years ago, intending to use it for his job. Goofing off one day, he found himself exploring the Internet. Andy visited various sites where people with common interests in books or sports or art gathered online to discuss their hobbies.

He fell into conversation with one particular person during his computer journey and soon found that they had much in common and thoroughly enjoyed conversing (albeit through a computer) with each other.

Weeks later, during a computer conversation with this new friend, Andy's house lost electrical power, shutting down his computer and cutting off his link to his friend. When the electricity came back on, Andy searched for his friend only to find that the friend, at the very same time, had also been cut off because of an electrical outage.

Suspicious about the coincidence, Andy and the friend decided to divulge their locations. Of all the places in the world the two of them could have been—with the computer capable of linking people on different continents, even on different sides of the Earth—it turned out that Andy and his friend lived on the very same street! When electricity went off on the street, it went off at both of their houses, which were just doors away from each other.

The lesson Andy learned is that there are wonderful people out there but also wonderful people right here—if you just take the opportunity to get to know them.

Close relationships, more than personal satisfaction or one's view of the world as a whole, are the most meaningful factors in happiness. If you feel close to other people, you are four times as likely to feel good about yourself than if you do not feel close to anyone.

Magen, Birenbaum, and Pery 1996

7

Turn off the TV.

Television is a creamy filling that distracts us from the substance of our lives.

When you are in the supermarket, do you buy something from each and every aisle? Of course not. You go to aisles that have something you want and skip the aisles that don't have anything you need. But when it comes to watching television, many of us seem to follow the buy-something-from-every-aisle plan. If it's Monday, we watch TV. If it's Tuesday, we watch TV. If it's Wednesday, we watch TV. Too often we watch TV because that's what we usually do rather than because there is something we actually want to see. Ask yourself when you are watching TV, "Is this something I want to see? Would I ask that this program be made if it didn't already exist?"

Psychologists have found some people who watch so much TV that it actually inhibits their ability to carry on a conversation. In the words of one psychologist, "TV robs our time and never gives it back."

Don't turn on the TV just because it's there and that's what you usually do. Turn it on only when there is something on that you want to watch. Your newly liberated hours can be spent doing something with your family or your friends or finding a rare quiet moment for yourself. Without TV, you can do something actively fun instead of passively distracting.

Watching too much TV can triple our hunger for more possessions, while reducing our personal contentment by about 5 percent for every hour a day we watch.

Wu 1998

8

Accept yourself—unconditionally.

You are not just the size of your bank account, the neighborhood you live in, or the type of work you do. You are, just like everyone else, an almost inconceivably complicated mix of abilities and limitations.

☺ ☺ ☺

A new kind of New Year's resolution is becoming increasingly popular. Instead of dwelling on something they think is wrong with them and resolving to improve, a lot of people are taking a different approach. They are resolving to accept themselves. To acknowledge that, faults and all, they are complete people, good people.

Kathleen, a member of a group that spreads the acceptance philosophy, explains that she used to feel like she was in a trap she could not get out of. She would try to correct herself and change herself, and the failure to change was actually worse than the original problem itself. She felt like a "maniac" because of the pressures to change and the weight of failure.

Now Kathleen counsels accepting yourself, which does not mean ignoring your faults or never trying to improve. What it does mean is "believing in your own value first, last, and always."

☺ ☺ ☺

In a study of adult self-esteem, researchers found that people who are happy with themselves take defeat and explain it away, treating it as an isolated incident that indicates nothing about their ability. People who are unhappy take defeat and enlarge it, making it stand for who they are and using it to predict the outcome of future life events.

Brown and Dutton 1995

9

Remember where you came from.

Think about and celebrate your ethnicity. Often we feel lost in a vast and complex world. There is tremendous comfort in knowing your ethnic heritage. It gives you a history, a sense of place, a uniqueness that remains no matter what else is going on around you.

☺ ☺ ☺

Our homes look the same, our towns look the same, we watch the same movies, we dress the same, we often seem indistinguishable from everyone else. We live in a time of mass-produced everything, and we often feel lost in all the sameness. We long to know how we fit into the world. Where did I come from, and how did I get to this place? Knowing our family history and our ethnic heritage can offer comfort because it helps tell us who we are, where we're from, and how we fit.

The Foundation for Empowerment is one good example. The group teaches African American children about their heritage with history lessons, art lessons, and celebrations of food and music.

What do the students get out of these lessons? Pride. A sense of accomplishment. A sense of place. The effects are impressive.

Students who participate tend to improve both their attendance and grades in school. As one eighth-grader explained, the program has made her work harder, be more committed to a professional career goal, and "feel better about myself because I know more about my heritage."

In studies of students, greater ethnic identity is associated with 10 percent greater life satisfaction.

Neto 1995

10

Limit yourself to thinking about one subject as you lie down to sleep.

Those who have a lot of anxiety let their thoughts shoot around from one subject to another as they try to go to sleep until, in a matter of minutes, they have created a virtual catalogue of problems. With all these problems, you'll ask yourself, how can I possibly sleep?

Tonight as you are brushing your teeth, come up with something you'd like to think about when you slip under the covers. If other thoughts start to intrude, guide yourself back to that one subject.

Megan hates junk mail. Not only does it waste her time, it also creates garbage. There's so much garbage! Megan doesn't know how people can throw out so much stuff. They say the landfills are nearly full.

Where will the garbage go then? It's not just garbage. There's all the waste from nuclear plants and toxic chemicals. What will the environment be like for the next generation? In two generations? Will the Earth survive? Can it possibly?

Too many of us allow our presleep thoughts to drift like this. Here Megan's minor annoyance leads to concerns about the future of the planet. And those concerns race around, causing stress instead of relaxation and sending people like Megan in search of sleep aids.

Too many thoughts, we now know, even if they don't lead to such a drastic topic as the fate of the Earth, are unsettling and make it much harder to sleep. When our thoughts bounce in and out, each idea backed by another, the stream of ideas makes us more on edge and less ready to close our eyes, shut off our brain for the day, and fall blissfully into sleep.

In studies of college students, shifting between pre-sleep thoughts was found to be related to difficulty in sleeping and lower sleep quality, which, in turn, were related to unhappiness. Better sleepers are 6 percent more satisfied with their lives than average sleepers, and 25 percent more satisfied than poor sleepers.

Abdel Khalek, Al-Meshaan, and Al-Shatti 1995

11

Friendship beats money.

If you want to know if people are happy, don't ask them how much money they have in the bank. Don't ask how large their take-home salary is. Ask them about their friends.

☺ ☺ ☺

Two financial advisers were in business together for over a decade, and then the market turned sour. They put everything they had into the business, but it wasn't enough, and soon they lost their business and all their money. When it was time to pick up the pieces, they both dwelled on the lost money and, in the process, lost their friendship.

Each blamed the other for the financial disaster. After not speaking to each other for over a year, though, they met each other for lunch. They both admitted to the other that they had experienced a major loss. And it wasn't the money, it was their friendship. One of them said, "Money is like a glove. Friendship is like your hand. One is useful, the other essential."

Contrary to the belief that happiness is hard to explain, or that it depends on having great wealth, researchers have identified the core factors in a happy life. The primary components are number of friends, closeness of friends, closeness of family, and relationships with co-workers and neighbors. Together these features explain about 70 percent of personal happiness.

Murray and Peacock 1996

12

Have realistic expectations.

People who are happy don't get everything they want, but they want most of what they get. In other words, they rig the game in their favor by choosing to value things that are within their grasp.

People who find themselves dissatisfied in life often set unreachable goals for themselves, setting themselves up to fail. Yet people who set high goals for themselves and reach them are no happier than people who set and reach more modest goals.

Whether you are assessing your position at work or your relationship with your family, don't begin with fantasy pictures of the world's richest person or the world's ideal family. Stay with reality and strive to make things better, not perfect.

There was a big retirement party for a high school principal, celebrating his thirty years of service to the Altoona, Pennsylvania, schools. People spoke eloquently of his wonderful contribution to thousands of children's education. At the end of the night of testimonials, he said to his friend, "When I was twenty-three, I thought I was eventually going to be president of the United States."

Here was a man who was universally respected, who had given himself to the vital calling of education, and who had risen through the ranks to lead a high school. And instead of reveling in his accomplishments, he was resigned to his defeats. He was by no means a failure—he was the opposite of failure—but in comparison with his immense and unreachable goals, he could not enjoy his success.

The congruence of people's goals with their resources strongly correlates with happiness. In other words, the more realistic and attainable people's goals are, the more likely they are to feel good about themselves. People who conclude their goals are out of reach are less than one-tenth as likely to consider themselves satisfied with life.

Diener and Fujita 1995

13

Be open to new ideas.

Never stop learning and adapting. The world will always be changing. If you limit yourself to what you knew and what you were comfortable with earlier in your life, you will grow increasingly frustrated with your surroundings as you age.

☺   ☺   ☺

You would see him around town from time to time. People knew him only as Herb. He was always walking by the side of the road. People asked him why he was always walking, and Herb told them he didn't believe in moving machines. Didn't own a car, wouldn't own a car, wouldn't take a cab or a bus.

Why? He said he got along just fine without them when he was younger, so why should he bother with them now? This belief provided him momentary comfort. He did not have to adapt, to face a change that he feared. However, he also shut himself off from everything that was not within a few miles of his house.

The world might as well not have existed for him, as he could not directly experience anything outside of his hometown. Principles are valuable and should be cherished, but there is a difference between principle and stubborn practice. As time went on and the lives of his children led them to scatter across the country, Herb consigned himself to never being able to visit them because he refused to adapt to the world as it exists.

In research on older Americans, what predicted satisfaction more than finances or the state of their current relationships was their willingness to adapt. If they were willing to change some of their habits and expectations, their happiness was maintained even when their circumstances changed. Those who were resistant to change, on the other hand, were less than one-third as likely to feel happy.

Clark, Carlson, Zemke, Gelya, Patterson, and Ennevor 1996

14

Share with others how important they are to you.

Relationships are built on mutual appreciation, and there is no better way to show that appreciation than to tell someone how much you care.

☺ ☺ ☺

Researchers at the University of Houston have studied the question of why we don't tell people how important they are to us. One area they studied was reaction to sad events like funerals.

One subject, Bill, lost a close family member recently. Some of Bill's friends sent sympathy cards, some sent flowers, some sent notes, some told him they were there for him. And some did nothing.

Why did some of his friends not say anything?

Perhaps they thought that telling others we care means being vulnerable. For these people, relationships may be more of a competition than a celebration, and competitions are premised on strength, power, and position.

Researchers caution that we don't win at relationships, we win by having relationships.

Research on unemployed adults has found that the length of unemployment was less important to a person's self-esteem than the amount of social support received from parents, family members, and friends.

Lackovic-Grgin and Dekovic 1996

15

If you're not sure, guess positively.

Unhappy people take a situation in which they are not sure and come to a negative conclusion. For example, if they aren't certain why another person is being nice, they assume that the person must have a hidden selfish agenda. Happy people take that same situation and guess the positive possibility, that is, that the person really is nice.

Henry is a seventy-year-old man who always had a good word for his neighbors. He lived modestly in Arkansas in a small home with only a wood stove for heat. Over the years, Henry watched his home deteriorate steadily. But he was too old and had too little money to fix it up. One of his neighbors organized a group to virtually rebuild Henry's house, giving it modern heat and plumbing. Henry was stunned by this. Why were all these people taking such an interest in him, in his house? He initially wondered, What did they stand to gain? Were they trying to change his house so that it would make their houses worth more?

Any situation can be viewed as an act of selfishness, if that's how you want to view it. Taking this perspective makes us cold, critical, and cynical. And there's no way out of it, because a person we view negatively cannot do anything to improve our impression of them. We need to consider that our perspective on what motivates people can either be a source of comfort to us or a source of alarm.

Henry's ultimate conclusion: "These were just good people doing a good thing, and I thank them for it."

Happy people and unhappy people explain the world differently. When an unhappy person must interpret the world, eight in ten times he or she will see the negative in an event. When a happy person must interpret the world, eight in ten times he or she will see the positive.

Brebner 1995

16

Believe in yourself.

Don't write yourself off. If you don't believe in yourself, you won't be able to function.

Steve Blass was a great major league pitcher in 1972. In fact, he was one of the very best. One year later, he was on his way out of baseball. Did he get hurt? No. Did anything change?

One thing changed: Steve Blass lost his confidence. As Blass said, "When it was gone, it was gone for good." He started thinking about all the things that could go wrong, and suddenly they did. Steve Blass no longer believed he could be a major league pitcher, and before he knew it, he no longer was a major league pitcher.

The ability to do anything must be accompanied by the belief that we *can* do it. As important as learning how is learning that you know how. There is an old saying, "Whether you believe you can or you believe you can't, either way you're right."

Across all ages and all groups, a solid belief in one's own abilities increases life satisfaction by about 30 percent, and makes us happier both in our home lives and in our work lives.

Myers and Diener 1995

17

Don't believe in yourself too much.

Believing in yourself means thinking you are a capable person, not that you will never make a mistake. Don't think that because you are a talented person you cannot learn from others or you should never be criticized or others want to know how highly you think of yourself.

A very rich fellow ran for governor of a Southern state not too long ago. He didn't like taking directions from people. He was, after all, his own man. He had become very successful on his own, and he thought there was nothing useful anyone could teach him because he already knew everything he needed to know.

Two things came out of this belief. One, people felt that he was full of himself, disagreeable, and not someone they particularly liked or trusted. And, two, when during a debate televised statewide he didn't know the answer to how the state passed a budget, people felt like his pompous image was a phony mask covering up for the fact that he really wasn't that capable. This man didn't become governor or senator or anything else he ran for. He told people he was too capable to listen and learn. The people told him he was just incapable of listening and learning.

☺   ☺   ☺

In studies on married couples, a significant connection is found between rigidity in one partner and discord in the relationship. Where one partner is convinced he or she is correct and therefore not open to suggestion, the length of time disagreements continue is about three times as great.

Botwin, Buss, and Shackelford 1997

18

Don't face your problems alone.

Problems can appear to be unsolvable. We are social creatures who need to discuss our problems with others, whether it be those who care about us most or those who have faced the same problems we have. When we are alone, problems fester. By sharing, we can gain perspective and find solutions.

It is a familiar story that the folks at Credit Counseling hear all too often. It goes like this: Sam missed a mortgage payment. Then he missed a second. Then he missed a third. Then the bank came and took his house away.

When he missed the first payment, all kinds of things could have been done. Arrangements could have been made that would have protected Sam and his house. Sam had friends who knew the rules, who could have helped. Sam didn't ask. He was embarrassed. He got himself into trouble, and he was going to get himself out of trouble.

Problem was, Sam didn't know how to get himself out of trouble. He didn't know what to do, and as days passed and his situation grew more grave, Sam only became more upset, more embarrassed. As a consequence, he isolated himself even more from his friends. Before they knew what hit Sam, he was out the door. Credit Counseling's counselors tell people, "The only thing that hiding your problems accomplishes is making sure no one helps you with them."

An experiment was conducted with a group of women having low life satisfaction. Some of the women were introduced to others who shared their situation, and some of the women were left on their own to deal with their concerns. Those who interacted with others saw a 55 percent reduction in their concerns over time, while those who were left on their own showed no improvement.

Hunter and Liao 1995

19

Age is not to be feared.

Older people are as happy as younger people. While they must make accommodations for age, seniors often report serene satisfaction with their life.

Mr. Nelson, as he is known, is a familiar fixture in his South Florida neighborhood. You always see him in his garden or taking his daily afternoon bicycle ride. He seems to be friends with everyone and always has a story to tell when you stop to talk to him.

If you ask him, he'll tell you that he has a cherished routine that fills his day with activities he enjoys. Mr. Nelson is ninety years old.

Far from regretting his age, he revels in it. He feels the wisdom of his years, and instead of facing the responsibilities that younger people with jobs have, he has little to worry about.

When people ask him about his age, he smiles and says, "I'm old, yes, but consider the alternative."

Surveys and an analysis of previous studies show that age is simply unrelated to levels of personal happiness.

Kehn 1995

20

Develop a household routine.

We often feel overwhelmed by the chores that have to be done on a regular basis. We clean the kitchen, then the living room needs to be vacuumed, the yard needs to be mowed, and sixteen other things need to be done. Set up a reasonable schedule to do your work, and instead of facing an endless chore, you will have a list of tasks to accomplish each day. With a routine, you will not be lost in wondering what's next.

Ernie is a teacher. He often tells his students that while he loves teaching, a part of him would love to be a builder. What is so great about builders? Ernie admires the fact that builders have to do things in an orderly process. They start by laying the foundation, then they put up the walls, the roof, the floors. Not only is it orderly, it is also easy for builders to assess their progress. At any time, builders can immediately see what has been accomplished.

Ernie tells his students that when they take on tasks, especially major recurring chores like homework or housework, they need to emulate builders. We need to set an order for things that need to be done; otherwise we tend to start one job, get distracted by something else, then look around and feel like we haven't accomplished anything. When we approach tasks like a builder, we finish what we start, and every step of the way we can see that we are closer to being finished.

In studies of families, regularity in household routines improved daily personal satisfaction by about 5 percent.

Henry and Lovelace 1995

21

Don't be overprotective.

None of us wants our loved ones to experience any harm, but we have to let them lead their lives. Spending our time worrying and trying to prevent them from doing what they want is a real risk in itself and will keep us worrying all the time.

Everything, absolutely everything, has a risk associated with it.

Some people become racked with fear over the possible dangers for themselves, their loved ones, and their children. Think about this for a moment: over the last seven years fear of crime has dramatically risen, while the actual crime rate has fallen.

People have become more afraid even as they have less to be worried about. The danger, as Franklin Roosevelt once suggested, is that the fear can become worse than the thing feared.

Not leaving the house or keeping the kids from playing a sport or avoiding other things because we are afraid is no solution for possible danger. It is only a different danger. While we certainly need to make sensible decisions, we need to consider the downside of avoiding the things that make life worthwhile.

Studies of thousands of parents found that there were negatives associated with being very protective, including increased time spent worrying and a generally higher level of stress. In sum, being more protective does not offer people more life satisfaction or contentment.

Voydanoff and Donnelly 1998

22

Pay attention.
You may have what you want.

We often forget to sit down and think about where we started and where we are now. The human tendency is to always want more. A better approach is to remember where you started and appreciate how much you have accomplished.

☺   ☺   ☺

Arthur was a hard-charging advertising executive. After three promotions in five years, he was working longer hours than ever before. He had gotten closer and closer to the top, and he could almost taste it now. Six-day workweeks with long hours were not enough, so he brought work home with him.

When he woke up in the recovery room after a triple bypass heart operation, he began to reassess. During three weeks of recovery, his family and best friends saw more of him than they had in decades. He cherished the time.

Arthur's wife asked him if he really needed to work the schedule he had. Did they need more money? Did he really need another promotion? Arthur, challenged to actually think about his life—something he never took the time to do when he was working—realized he had more than he needed and that the opportunity to reconnect with his family was the greatest gift he could be given.

In research on highly educated professionals, almost half of the subjects could not become satisfied even as they accomplished their apparent goals because they did not recognize their accomplishments and instead created an irrational negative image of themselves.

Thurman 1981

23

Don't let your religious beliefs fade.

Religion can show us the way in a world in which bad things happen. It can teach us that much of what we see is so complex we cannot understand why and how it occurred.

Everywhere in our world there is mystery. Everywhere there are questions. Religion offers answers, religion offers consistency, religion offers hope.

Doris is in her seventies and has had two heart attacks and cancer. By any normal medical calculation, she would be dead. Instead, she visits with her grandchildren and takes time to meet with medical students to discuss the importance of religious faith to her survival. Doris believes that without her religion she wouldn't have survived.

Skeptical? It's just one woman's opinion, after all.

Researchers at the Harvard Medical School, the National Institutes of Health, and countless other centers have backed up her claim. Active religious practices, their studies find, are associated with longer, healthier, and, yes, happier lives.

While doctors don't necessarily understand why this is, Father McGlone, a priest, thinks religion is important "not because we know all the answers, but because we have the best answer there is: faith."

Research on the effect of religion on life satisfaction found that regardless of what religion people affiliated themselves with, those who had strongly held spiritual beliefs were typically satisfied with life, while those who had no spiritual beliefs typically were unsatisfied.

Gerwood, LeBlanc, and Piazza 1998

24

Do what you say you are going to do.

Nothing kills progress or deadens enthusiasm more than someone who talks but never follows through. It is crucial in both your home life and your work life that you stay focused and committed to whatever you say you will do.

A used car salesman shows you a car. The odometer reads 07,000. The car is about five years old. You think the car has 107,000 miles on it, but the used car salesman says that it really has just 7,000 miles; it was owned by a little old lady, and she hardly ever drove it. Do you believe the salesman?

Probably you think about all the stories you've heard about dishonest people who sell cars, and you dismiss the salesman's story. Used car salesmen lack a fundamental necessity for positive communication: credibility.

We need to believe people tell the truth if we are going to interact with them, listen to them, trust them. The same rule applies in your own family settings and work settings. You cannot break your promises and expect to continue to be credible, even if you have the best intentions.

It's important to remember, credibility is like the bottom of a ship. If it has holes, it doesn't matter whether they are big or little—they all matter.

The difference between those who have happy personal relationships and those who have unhappy personal relationships is not the amount of conflicts they have. Indeed, each group has a similar number of conflicts. Instead, it is a greater commitment to following through on agreed-upon changes that contributes to the success of relationships and the 23 percent greater happiness of the individuals involved.

Turner 1994

25

Don't be aggressive with your friends and family.

Even if you are right, there is nothing to be gained from letting yourself become adversarial with your loved ones. Remember how much more important these people are to you than is the issue you are talking about.

☺ ☺ ☺

It would be great to always be right, wouldn't it?

Adam is always right. At least, he thinks so. Whether it's a matter of a trivia question or the best way to hang wallpaper, Adam knows the answer. When his family challenges him on some point, any point, Adam launches an inquest. He asks people to tell him why they disagree, and then he tries to catch them in an inconsistency. His follow-up questions are like those used by a lawyer trying to get an unreliable witness to admit his faults.

Adam almost always wins. He almost always gets a concession from his witness. The problem is, Adam's witness is not a criminal in a courtroom but a friend or loved one who holds a different opinion. Some of his friends have concluded it's just not worth disagreeing with Adam, and others have concluded it's not even worth talking to Adam, since you never know when a topic will lead to a controversy. Adam wins all the little battles, but he loses the metaphorical war. He loses the opportunity to spend enjoyable time with those he cares about.

Prevalent criticism within relationships reduces happiness up to one-third.

O'Connor 1995

26

Root for the home team.

Living with the ups and downs of your area's favorite sports team will help you feel a part of the community and show you how much you have in common with your neighbors.

People in southern Indiana root for the Indiana University basketball team. Almost everybody roots for the Hoosiers. What's neat about that is that people from all walks of life immediately have something in common. The mechanic and the doctor, the schoolteacher and the chef, the janitor and the mayor may not have a lot of similar interests, but they can all discuss Indiana's season.

The team gives the community the chance not only to hold a common interest but also to come together on game day. And when the team plays away games, it's not unusual to see house after house tuned to the game. Walk down the street and you'll hear conversations about the team and immediately feel that you are a part of the community, that something binds you and your neighbors and the rest of the city together.

Stanley, a lifelong Indiana fan, planned his wedding around the Indiana basketball schedule. His wife-to-be didn't mind, though; they had met at an Indiana game. And other than getting married at halftime, she wouldn't have had it any other way.

Rooting for a local sports team was found to have positive effects by providing a common interest with others in the community and increasing happiness by 4 percent.

Shank and Beasley 1998

27

Don't confuse stuff with success.

You are neither a better nor worse person for the kind of car you drive, the size of your home, or the performance of your mutual funds. Remember what really matters in your life.

☺   ☺   ☺

Imagine for a moment that today was your last day on Earth. Now, make a list for yourself of all the things that you feel you have accomplished, all the things you are proud of, and all the things that make you happy.

Is your car on the list? Your television? Your stereo? Is your salary on the list? No. What's on the list are the fundamental elements of a satisfied life—your relationship with friends and family, the contribution you have made to others' lives, the celebrated events of your life. Those are the building blocks of your list.

Many of us live day to day as if the opposite were true. Instead of appreciating what is truly important and making that our priority, we collect things and indicators of success without questioning just what success really means.

In a study using surveys and daily observation, the availability of material resources was nine times less important to happiness than the availability of "personal" resources such as friends and family.

Diener and Fujita 1995

28

Every relationship is different.

If you've been disappointed by strained relations with a friend or loved one, you must realize that each relationship is unique. Don't let tension with one person convince you that you lack the ability to be a good friend or a loving family member.

Jane has a good relationship with her parents and her brother. With her sister, though, she has never really gotten along. She is frustrated by this, always questioning why she can't duplicate the easy times she has with her parents and her brother. What's wrong with me? Jane asks herself. But what Jane does that makes her parents so happy and her brother so happy has the opposite effect on her sister. What is funny and charming to the rest of her family is seen as phony by her sister. To change to please her sister, though, would not only be difficult, it would alter the positive relationships Jane has.

Why can't we take our positive relationships that we enjoy with some people and duplicate them with everyone we know? The answer, say psychologists at Canada's McGill University, is that "people are too complex, they have too many facets" to be expected to react the same way as each other.

What can we do? We need to accept that our getting along with most but not all our loved ones is not a flaw but a reality. The university researchers explain, "More satisfied people do not have happy relationships with everyone. They appreciate their happy relationships and accept their imperfect relationships."

Researchers found there were no differences in overall happiness between those who mainly relied upon friends for companionship and those who mainly relied upon family. People have the capacity to create happiness from the relationships available to them and do not need all their relationships to fit an ideal image.

Takahashi, Tamura, and Tokoro 1997

29

Don't think "what if."

Spending your time imagining what would have been if you could have changed some little thing, some little decision in your life, is counterproductive and leaves you unhappy. Think about how you can improve for the future, but don't waste your present thinking about how you could have changed the past.

We could trace our current position to every decision we have ever made. Where you sat in kindergarten influenced who your friends were, which influenced what your interests were, which influenced how you did in school, and so forth.

We could ponder these things endlessly, but it wouldn't get us anywhere. Take a wrong turn on your way somewhere, and it won't pay to pull over and question why or how you took the wrong turn. What you need to do is think about how you can get from where you are to where you want to be.

The same applies to your life: don't wallow in disappointment over how you got to where you are. Think about what you need to do to get where you want to be.

Research on athletes who came close but lost in Olympic finals finds that those who spend the least time on counterfactual thought—thinking about how things might have ended differently—are the most satisfied with their experience.

Gilovich and Medvec 1995

30

Volunteer.

Every community has countless opportunities for giving of yourself. Be a reading tutor. Give your time to help the local charity thrift store. Anything you can do will not only help the world, it will also help you. Volunteers feel good about themselves. They have a sense of purpose, feel appreciated, and are less likely to be bored in their lives. Volunteers experience rewards that cannot be attained in any other way. Even if you don't have a lot of time or skills, find an hour a month and give yourself to a good cause.

Bessie is a widow in her seventies. She found herself with time on her hands and a desire to do something useful with it. She wanted something that would make her want to get up in the morning with a smile on her face.

Bessie found out about a foster grandparent program run out of a Buffalo area community center. The program uses senior citizens to offer companionship to disabled children during the day.

Bessie signed up and now spends a couple of hours a day playing, reading, talking, and sitting with the children.

One of Bessie's friends, who also volunteers in the same program, says that the foster grandparents give the children "love and attention," and in return they are rewarded by getting a chance to see "the beauty in every one of these children."

Bessie says the volunteer work "gives me the feeling that I am doing something good. I'm helping the children, the parents, and myself. Everybody wins, but I always feel I win the most."

An analysis of volumes of previous research on the subject shows a strong consensus that volunteering contributes to happiness by decreasing boredom and creating an increased sense of purpose in life. Volunteers, on average, are twice as likely to feel happy with themselves as non-volunteers.

Crist-Houran 1996

31

If you can't reach your goals, your goals will hurt you.

People who cannot attain their goals become consumed with disappointment. You must let your goals evolve with your life circumstances. Update your goals over time as you consider your changing priorities and resources.

University of Michigan psychologists have found great evidence that while goals are important, goals can do us a great disservice if they are not flexible. Here's a typical story.

Jimmy proposed to his girlfriend when he was only eighteen. She accepted, and they were married a year later. At the time, Jimmy promised that he would buy them a house before he turned twenty-four. Jimmy took the first in a series of jobs. None of them paid very well. Jimmy and his bride lived in a modest but comfortable apartment. As the clock ticked on, though, Jimmy saved as much as he could, got down-payment money from his parents, and eked out a mortgage approval. Jimmy and his wife moved in, and then they celebrated. The payments were more than he could afford, though.

Soon he took on a second job. It wasn't enough.

Jimmy took another part-time job, his third.

He worked himself sick and over time began to resent both the house and the wife that he had promised it to.

Instead of continuing a life he found satisfying and continuing to save for a house someday, Jimmy rushed the process to meet his declared goal. He let a rigid goal change his life, which was the same as letting a rigid goal harm his life.

If a person's goals are incongruent with his or her abilities, then the goals will contribute to disappointment and disagreeableness, and will quadruple the likelihood of being dissatisfied.

Pavot, Fujita, and Diener 1997

32

Exercise.

People who exercise, whether that involves an intense workout or just a regular long walk, feel healthier, feel better about themselves, and enjoy life more.

☺   ☺   ☺

A prominent executive used to say, "Whenever the thought occurs to me that maybe I should exercise, I lie down until the thought passes."

He said this a lot, and, not surprisingly, his philosophy led him directly to a lack of energy and, soon, to health problems.

His doctors impressed on him the necessity of changing his lifestyle, and the executive gave it a try. To his surprise, he found he actually enjoyed exercising. It was a chance to spend some time every day, without any worries or concerns, doing something positive. And instead of making him tired, exercise actually increased his energy.

What's his philosophy now? "I enjoy exercise so much, I can hardly put it into words."

Research on physical activity finds that exercise increases self-confidence, which in turn strengthens self-evaluations. Regular exercise, including brisk walks, directly increases happiness 12 percent, and can indirectly make a dramatic contribution to improving self-image.

Fontane 1996

33

Little things have big meanings.

Tiny things—the tone of your voice, the exact words you use as you go through otherwise ordinary events—communicate volumes.

Do little things, like a slight change in your facial expression, really matter?

Humans don't swell up like blowfish or change colors like chameleons. Our reactions are seen in more subtle expressions, tones of voice, and body language.

Consider this: recognizing someone's facial expression takes less than one-sixth of a second. We can process expressions from as far as 100 yards away. How can we do this? We pay attention. Humans are attuned to facial expressions as an indicator of what their companions are thinking. Because we think facial expressions are important, we pay attention to them. Because we pay attention to facial expressions, we react to them. Because we react, facial expressions become important to our communication.

The next time someone asks you if you like the dinner they made, and you say "It's good," remember the other person is paying attention not only to what you say, but also to other messages you might be communicating.

Married couples who display sensitivity in communication—who recognize the power of subtle changes in demeanor—rate their satisfaction 17 percent higher than couples who do not.

Notarius 1996

34

It's not what happened, it's how you think about what happened.

There is no objective way to tell you if you have had a good life, a good day, or a good hour. Your life is a success based only upon your judgment.

A study was done recently in which people on opposite sides of an issue where given the same newspaper article to read. The people were asked to read the article carefully and to offer their reaction. On average, people said they thought the article was biased—against their own position. That is, people on both sides of the issue thought the exact same article was biased against their side. The article could not possibly have been biased against both sides of the issue. Obviously, it wasn't the content of the article that drove the reaction, but the perspective of the readers. Life events have the same effect. The same event can be seen positively, or it can be seen negatively. It depends upon your perspective.

Knowing whether someone has recently suffered a personal setback or personal triumph is not as good a predictor of how satisfied they are with their lives as is knowing how they perceive the causes and consequences of those events.

Staats, Armstrong-Stassen, and Partillo 1995

35

Develop some common interests with loved ones.

Common interests can make it more fun to be around your family and friends. They can allow you to see that your bonds are much deeper than just circumstance.

☺   ☺   ☺

Every member of Tom's family loves jumping out of planes. "It may be strange to some people, but it's really a nice way to spend the day together with your family," explained Tom.

Tom and his son first tried skydiving together, and they enjoyed it so much they decided to take lessons together so they could learn to jump without a guide.

Soon Tom's wife and their daughter were joining them—with the whole family jumping out of planes together.

On a typical weekend, the family spends hours together traveling to and from the jump site, and they might jump out of their plane four or five times.

Tom's family loves the fun of their hobby, and they love the chance it gives them to spend time together. Tom and his wife even renewed their wedding vows at 4,000 feet, before jumping out of the plane together, as their children and guests looked on.

Each common interest between people in a relationship increases the likelihood of a lasting relationship and results in an increase in life satisfaction of about 2 percent.

Chand 1990

36

Laugh.

Don't spend your time evaluating humor, asking yourself, "Is it really funny?" or "Do others think it's funny?" Just react and enjoy it.

☺ ☺ ☺

A group called the American Association for Therapy and Humor believes that one of the things too often missing from our days is a good laugh.

The message is being heard by an increasing number of business consultants, who find that a little laughter makes for a better employee.

Businesses across the country have Dress Like Elvis Days, clown squads that roam the halls sharing mirth, and silly contests like seeing who can throw a paper airplane the farthest.

Why?

Shaking us out of our routine increases creativity, productivity, and job satisfaction.

But whether at work or at home, the Therapy and Humor group says, "Happiness is a laughing matter."

In studies of hundreds of adults, happiness was found to be related to humor. The ability to laugh, whether at life itself or at a good joke, is a source of life satisfaction. Indeed, those who enjoy silly humor are one-third more likely to feel happy.

Solomon 1996

37

Don't let your entire life hinge on one element.

Your life is made up of many different facets. Don't focus on one aspect of your life so much that you can't experience pleasure if that one area is unsettled. It can become all you think about, and it can deaden your enjoyment of everything else—things you would otherwise love.

Would you invest every dollar you had in the stock of one company?

Of course not. Every expert you could possibly consult would tell you to invest by diversifying. You shouldn't place all your hopes on one company or even one kind of company. Instead, you should intelligently pursue a variety of investments, with no one central investment capable of ruining your savings.

The same applies to living your life: you should diversify your hopes.

Don't pin all your hopes on getting a promotion and wind up ruining what could have been a satisfying home life by lack of progress in the office.

Don't define your life based on having a perfect relationship with one family member and wind up feeling devastated by a strained relationship.

Build your hopes around the many things that are important to you, and allow yourself to benefit from the different things that contribute to your life, rather than allowing yourself to be devastated by a single bump in the road.

In an experiment in which subjects were asked to discuss the life satisfaction of others, subjects tended to calculate likelihood of happiness on an "averaging" scale. That is, happiness was associated with people whose lives were generally positive in multiple areas that mattered to them.

Bhargava 1995

38

Share of yourself.

Don't hold inside your feelings, your thoughts, your hopes. Share them with your friends and family. People who hold things inside tend to feel isolated, believing that others do not understand them. Those who share feel both supported and more content, even if events do not go exactly as they wish.

Rose has been an artist for many years. In her spare time she would paint beautiful watercolor landscapes. From time to time, she would display her work in the local art show or have some of her pieces shown in a small art shop and gallery. Whenever her family asked her about her art, their question was either "Did you sell anything?" or "How much did you make?" Rose felt like this wonderful form of expression, this way of being herself that was so important to her, was completely misunderstood. She wasn't trying to make money, she didn't care if it sold. She painted for herself, not for profit. Every time she was asked whether she made any money, she would churn inside.

Why don't they understand me? Rose wondered. Why do these people, who should be so close to me, seem so distant and removed? These thoughts grew inside of her and caused her to become less comfortable around her family. Then Rose realized that her family couldn't read her mind and that part of the reason they didn't understand her was that she hadn't explained what was really important to her.

Individuals who tend to be socially open rate their overall life satisfaction 24 percent higher than individuals who do not.

Finch, Barrera, Okun, Bryant, Pool, and Snow-Turek 1997

39

Busy is better than bored.

Find something to do, because the feeling that we have too much to do is much more pleasing than the feeling that we have nothing to do.

A philosopher once noted that people long for immortality but run out of things to do on a rainy afternoon. If we planned out our time in long chunks, say twenty years, we would never consider penciling in five or ten of those years for wasting time. Yet during the average day, we often let a few hours slip away. Time is a strange commodity, because we seem to have so much of it, until the moment we have none at all. We often complain about having too much to do. Yet having too much to do is a positive problem of abundance, while having too little to do is a negative problem of shortage.

Metro Plastics Technology in Indiana tested out this principle by cutting the length of the workweek for its employees from forty hours to thirty hours. And do you know what happened after the switch? The quality of the company's products improved, and the company actually made more money. Management found that giving workers more to do in less time made the workers more efficient, energetic, and enthusiastic and gave workers more free time outside of the workplace.

☺ ☺ ☺

In studies of college students, those with more demanding schedules were 15 percent more satisfied with life. Despite the more demanding schedules, the individuals studied did not experience any more stress than those with less to do.

Bailey and Miller 1998

40

Satisfaction is relative.

Your happiness is relative to a scale you yourself have created. If you measure your satisfaction right now against the two or three greatest moments in your life, you will often be unhappy because those moments can't be duplicated. If you measure today's satisfaction against some tough days you've had, you have all the reason in the world to appreciate this moment.

Is Bobby a good student? Well, are you comparing him to his classmates or to Einstein? Is Harrison Ford a good actor? Well, are you comparing him to Keanu Reeves or to Robert DeNiro? Was today a good day? Well, are you comparing it to graduations, weddings, and celebrations, or to your typical Tuesday? We need to consider things in a realistic perspective.

Anthropologists at Rutgers University are finding that one of the most significant determinants of people's enjoyment of work is their feelings about their home life. Many people are finding their work more tolerable because their family situations have become more stressful.

The Rutgers team finds that people are clinging to the order and friendship available in the workplace and that the often hectic, pressure-filled home life suffers by comparison.

The sad reality, of course, is that your home life cannot duplicate those aspects of the workplace and shouldn't be expected to. Jobs should be compared to other jobs but not to the home, where everything is both more complex, and offers more potential rewards.

A good day on the job should be thought of relative to other days on the job. A good day at home should be thought of relative to other days at home.

Not surprisingly, surveys find that happy people tend to have more positive experiences than unhappy people. What is striking is that, objectively, their lives aren't really much different. Studies find that happy people experience much the same range of events as unhappy people. The real difference is in what they define as positive and negative. Happy people are those who use a lower threshold in order to label an event positive.

Parducci 1995

41

Learn to use a computer.

Whether they are eight or ninety-eight, people who use computers experience the wonders of technology and of the world.

Computers can help bring people together, and nowhere is that more important than for people who are constantly being moved apart. For example, computers allow access to e-mail, and these instant messages are becoming crucial to military families, who often have to live apart from one another and who even more regularly must settle in new communities apart from their friends.

Melody, a fifth-grader whose father is in the army, has recently lived in Kentucky, Illinois, Texas, and Colorado. While she finds it hard to always move away and sometimes watch friends move away, her computer lets her stay in touch with friends who are scattered across the country.

The army has found that computers have made military relocations a little bit easier for the entire family because they can use the computer to find out about their new home and to stay in touch with friends they are leaving behind.

☺ ☺ ☺

In a study of senior citizens introduced to personal computers, self-esteem and life satisfaction were found to improve by about 5 percent as a result of computer use.

Sherer 1996

42

Try to think less about the people and things that bother you.

There are an infinite number of things you could spend your time thinking about, but many of us concentrate great attention on those things that we find most upsetting. Don't ignore what bothers you, but don't focus on it to the exclusion of the things you enjoy.

Ralph owns the corner lot on a crowded Chicago block. He counts his immediate neighbors as friends. One of his neighbors is also his family doctor.

The problem is access to backyards. The houses are right on top of each other, and the only way any of his neighbors can drive to their backyards is through Ralph's yard. But Ralph often parks his car in his yard, which blocks the path of any of his neighbors to their yards. They can walk to their yards, they just can't drive there.

Do they really need to drive to their backyards? Not very often, but the fact that they couldn't because Ralph's car was in the way irritated some of them.

Ralph's neighbors researched the city ordinances and found an 1892 rule that appeared to grant them access to Ralph's yard to get to their own. Ralph said the 1892 rule gives them the right to walk through his backyard, not drive through it.

These friends and neighbors soon became neither, for they got together—including the family doctor—and sued Ralph for auto access to their backyards. Relationships deteriorated, all because no one was prepared to sacrifice something that wasn't really important for the sake of peace and friendship.

Those who regularly ruminate over negative subjects and unhappiness are 70 percent less likely to feel content than those who do not.

Scott and McIntosh 1999

43

Keep your family close.

As family members scatter across the country, it becomes easy to forget to include them in your thoughts and in your time. Keep up the contact, share with your family the news of your life. They want to know, and you will feel better if your bond is maintained.

☺   ☺   ☺

Two decades ago, Sally moved away from her family's home to go to college. Her mother recalls the time sadly: "It was horrible. I wanted her to pursue her dreams, but I didn't want to lose her. I felt that she wanted to abandon me, that she wanted to be gone."

Sally took her mother's reaction as a sign of her mother's insecurity instead of her love, and they grew apart. "She'd ask me why I'd gone so far away. I didn't process it. I felt it was her problem."

Sally's career kept her geographically distant from her family. Over time, Sally's mother showed less and less concern for Sally's decisions. Sally worried that her mother did not care, and their relationship remained as distant as their locations.

Then, Sally realized that beneath the initial concern and her mother's more recent reaction, was the same thing: love.

Geography now is no longer a barrier. Sally and her mother communicate regularly, and Sally cherishes the opportunity to visit her hometown. Sally cautions that both those who leave and those who stay have to remember that being apart does not have to mean being distant from each other.

Studies that examine the importance of family to senior citizens as compared to adults not yet entering middle age show family relationships to be an equally crucial component of life satisfaction for both age groups.

O'Connor 1995

44

Eat some fruit every day.

Fruit eaters feel good about what they eat, are less interested in eating junk food, and ultimately feel better about themselves.

Have you noticed that even though there are magazines that you would never buy and never go out of your way to read, you will pick them up when you're stuck in a waiting room? Out of desperation and convenience, we accept things that do not appeal to us. The same applies to what we eat. We're in a hurry, and we don't want to spend a lot of energy or time on food. Often it's like we're in that waiting room, going for the first food we see.

Keep fruit in the house, and eat it as a snack. It's easy, it's cheap, it requires no preparation time, and it's great for you. Study after study shows the physical benefits of eating fruit, and now we know it has emotional benefits as well. Our bodies crave sweet tastes, which originally was an evolutionary advantage, for it led early humans to consume more fruit. Only in modern times, when sugary sweets have become available to us, has our taste for sweets had negative consequences.

Eating fruit is associated with a number of positive life habits that contribute to both health and happiness, and eating more fruit is associated with an 11 percent higher likelihood of feeling capable and satisfied.

Heatey and Thombs 1997

45

Enjoy what you have.

People who are satisfied appreciate what they have in life and don't worry about how it compares to what others have. Valuing what you have over what you do not or cannot have leads to greater happiness.

☺ ☺ ☺

Four-year-old Alice runs to the Christmas tree and sees wonderful presents beneath it. No doubt she has received fewer presents than some of her friends, and probably she has not received some of the things she most wanted. But at that moment, she doesn't stop to think why aren't there more presents or to wonder what she may have asked for that she didn't get. Instead, she marvels at the treasures before her.

When we think about our lives, too often we think about what we don't have and what we didn't get. But such a focus denies us pleasure. You wouldn't sit next to the Christmas tree and remind Alice that there were presents she didn't receive. Why remind yourself of the things in life you don't have when you could remind yourself of what you do have?

People who have the most are only as likely to be happy as those who have the least. People who like what they have, however, are twice as likely to be happy as those who actually have the most.

Sirgy, Cole, Kosenko, and Meadow 1995

46

Think in concrete terms.

We need to be able to measure our progress, to know that things are improving. You can't accomplish an abstract goal, because you'll never be sure if you're finished or not.

I want to be a better worker. I want to be a better parent. I want to be a better friend. Many of us have these kinds of hopes—vague hopes. The problem with these kinds of ideas is that they are not specific. They include no step-by-step directions and no outcomes. You want to be a better worker. Well, what does that mean? How does someone do that? How will you know if you've succeeded or not?

StarQuest is a consulting firm in Houston that teaches goal setting—specifically, how to make your goals clear and direct. They advise you to think about what you care about, and then think about what you can actually do to accomplish that.

You might set as your goals: I want to finish this weekly report an hour faster; I want to make this task 5 percent cheaper; I want to have dinner with my family one more night per week; I want to make it to all my daughter's soccer games. Here your goals come with built-in directions. These are goals that you can work toward and successfully complete. Completing any goal we set for ourselves improves our confidence and satisfaction and steadies us for the future.

Perceptions that life is meaningful, and therefore worthwhile, increase 16 percent with concrete thinking.

Lindeman and Verkasalo 1996

47

Be socially supportive.

Take the time to help, comfort, or just be with those you care about when they are in need. You will feel good about your efforts, and it will bring you an even closer relationship.

Sarah wasn't sure she could make it through all her high school courses, then to college, on her way to a goal of becoming a teacher. Often it took her longer than any of her classmates to finish readings and assignments, and every step along the way was arduous.

Her friends spent many days helping Sarah, especially with her readings.

On graduation night Sarah, soon bound for an Ivy League school, thanked those friends for their help, faith, and support. She spoke to her classmates as the first blind valedictorian in school history.

The need for support or the number of problems individuals face is a less strong predictor of their happiness than the amount of support available to them.

Jou and Fukada 1997

48

Don't blame yourself.

When things go poorly, we sometimes start a list of ways we failed, ways we caused the problem. This kind of thinking not only can upset us, it also can keep us from being able to function. The truth is that any situation is the result of some things that are in your control and some things that are out of your control. Don't delude yourself into thinking a bad situation is completely of your making. Remember, it makes more sense to deal with outcomes than with fault.

Company is coming, and the dishwasher is spouting water. The flood is spreading across the kitchen floor, heading for the living room. You think to yourself, Why did I have to do the dishes right now? Or, If I had washed the dishes by hand, this wouldn't be happening. If I had waited to use the dishwasher tomorrow, it wouldn't be ruining my night now. It's obvious, if only I had sense enough to see the facts. Why did I even buy this dishwasher? I bet if I had gone with a different model, it wouldn't be flooding my kitchen right now!

When things go wrong we look to lay blame, and often we look in the mirror. Psychologists at the National Institute of

Mental Health find that many of us fall victim to the "everything is my fault" approach to life.

Two things we often overlook is how little we directly control a situation and how little value there is in spending our time blaming ourselves. These thoughts do not fix the problem. These thoughts do not make anything better. Blame is about the past; a plan of action to fix a problem is about the future.

Happiness does not depend on how many bad things happen to an individual. What is more important is whether an individual tends to make negative conclusions about him- or herself when negative events occur. Individuals who think of themselves as the cause of negative events are 43 percent less likely to be satisfied than individuals who do not.

Panos 1997

49

Be a peacemaker.

If your friends or family members are upset with one another, you will feel their unhappiness. Try to be the voice of reason and reconciliation.

☺   ☺   ☺

Nellie and Cindy are sisters from northern California. They were close all their lives, and they even decided to move in together to share Nellie's house.

And then the phone bill came.

Nellie received what she called the biggest phone bill of her life and immediately confronted her sister. Cindy looked at the bill and said that most of the calls weren't hers; they must have been placed by Nellie.

Words escalated, until the tension between the sisters completely eclipsed their familial bonds. The rest of their family members felt uncomfortable in their presence and began to avoid them rather than trying to help them through the difficulty.

With no compromise in sight, Nellie sued her own sister in small claims court. The family was exasperated with the both of them.

And even while Nellie won the case, she lost her sister.

☺ ☺ ☺

The passive avoidance of problems between loved ones reduces contentment by 15 percent. To keep in contact and maintain happiness, difficulties must be faced rather than avoided.

Simpson 1990

50

Cherish animals.

Animals have so much to teach us about love. The closer we get to animals, the more joy they give us.

Gina runs a nursing home. She has tried all kinds of things to brighten the days for her senior citizens. What works better than anything else is dogs.

The local animal shelter brings in a vanload of small dogs every Thursday afternoon, and the seniors immediately smile. The dogs offer unconditional love, and the residents of the nursing home, who often feel isolated and withdrawn, take that love and are energized by it. Softened by the love, they return it right back to their furry friends.

"You just have to watch one of these dogs put his head under a listless hand, demanding to be petted, or rest his chin on a patient's chest and stare lovingly into their eyes, or see someone who wouldn't get out of bed offer to hold the leash and take a dog for a walk down the hall" to see how much dogs can help, according to one volunteer. "You can actually see dogs bring people out of themselves and help them forget their troubles. Blank faces come alive, and eyes uncloud."

☺ ☺ ☺

Interaction with animals supplies us with both immediate joy and long-term positive feelings, and contributes strongly to our happiness. Those with a loved pet are 22 percent more likely to feel satisfied than those without.

Barofsky and Rowan 1998

51

Make your work a calling.

If you see your work as only a job, then it's dragging you away from what you really want to be doing. If you see it as a calling, then it is no longer a toiling sacrifice. Instead, it becomes an expression of you, a part of you.

☺   ☺   ☺

Victor is a motorman for the Chicago Transit Authority. Five days a week he's running an elevated train on the Red Line. Victor stands out in the minds of the people who ride his train because of a notable and unusual trait: he loves his job.

"Thank you for riding with me this evening on Electric Avenue. Don't lean against the doors, I don't want to lose you," he tells passengers over the intercom as the train departs.

As the train makes its way north, Victor points out notable sites, including which connecting buses are waiting in the street below.

People compliment him all the time, telling the city he's the best motorman in Chicago.

Victor admits, "Our equipment may be junky, but for $1.50 I want to give a Lincoln Town Car ride."

Why does Victor have such a positive approach to his job? "My father is a retired motorman, and one day he took me to work with him and I was so impressed looking out that window," he says, speaking of the city skyline. "Ever since I was five years old, I knew I wanted to run the trains."

In research on working women, researchers found that even for those working in the same kinds of jobs, work was alternatively viewed either as a series of hassles or as a positive experience in which the women were in control of their lives. Among those who felt control, life satisfaction was 28 percent higher than among those who did not.

Thakar and Misra 1995

52

Never trade your morals for your goals.

People who compromise what they believe in to satisfy their goals wind up dissatisfied with their accomplishments. If you do not believe yourself to be moral, satisfaction is unattainable.

A few years back, a student at Yale was expelled. His transgression was that he had faked all the documents in his application: his grades, his letters of recommendation, his activities. His fake application looked so good that Yale admitted him.

The student actually did well in his classes and was nearing graduation.

How did he get caught? He confessed. He simply could not keep quiet about his fake application, even though his real course work was about to get him a degree. The fact that his achievement would always be predicated on a lie made it no achievement at all.

Being happy and being moral buttress each other. People who feel they lack morals report they are half as likely to feel happy compared to those who feel they are moral.

Garrett 1996

53

Don't pretend to ignore things your loved ones do that bother you.

In the name of being agreeable, some people try to avoid areas that might cause dissension. But with our loved ones, this strategy sometimes makes us uncomfortable. We can feel unappreciated because we have made a sacrifice but nobody thanks us for it. Sometimes we feel angry because this problem doesn't go away. Raise the subject of your disagreement, but do so lovingly and constructively, not with anger or aggression.

☺ ☺ ☺

Mary is a hairdresser. Her sister Kim is a banker. Normally, this is of little importance to Mary. But Mary's mother introduces her daughters to friends this way: "Mary's a hairdresser. Her sister's a banker, though." Inside it burns Mary every time. Why does her mother have to focus on her daughters' occupations and then say it in a way that makes it sound like she's disappointed in Mary's work?

Inevitably, when Mary visits her mother, her mother complains that Mary is unfriendly or "too down." She never considers that it is her own comments that put Mary in that state.

Mary finally explained how her mother's words felt to her, and her mother said she had no idea. She was proud of both of her daughters, and she didn't intend to make it seem that her daughters' occupations were what mattered to her.

In relationships, those who feel they can freely communicate their concerns and needs to their partner are 40 percent more likely to feel satisfied than those who do not.

Ferroni and Taffe 1997

54

Get a good night's sleep.

Don't skimp on sleep. A full night's rest is fuel for the following day. Rested people feel they work better and are more comfortable when the day is over.

☺   ☺   ☺

An interesting thing happened on Tuesday mornings in the fall of 1998. A study found that workers in the Northeast were 3 percent more productive than they had been on Tuesdays the autumn before.

What changed? Monday night football came on an hour earlier in 1998, and more men got a decent night's sleep as a result. Instead of games lasting past midnight, in 1998 games tended to end before 11:30.

Sleep is such an easy thing to trade away to TV, to work, to anything. Sleep seems like the bottomless bank account we can never overdraw. But a good night's sleep pays dividends in every aspect of our lives.

Quality and quantity of sleep contribute to health, well-being, and a positive outlook. For those who sleep less than eight hours, every hour of sleep sacrificed results in an 8 percent less positive feeling about their day.

Pilcher and Ott 1998

55

Buy what you like.

Don't accumulate possessions for the sake of having a lot of stuff. On the other hand, don't deny yourself something that you really want or need. If you buy things that are important to you, you can appreciate them every day and won't feel the need to fill your home with every item at the mall.

In a single year, Americans buy over 17 billion articles of clothing. Americans buy so much new clothing that every year we give over 200 million pounds of clothing away to the Salvation Army alone. Americans buy so much new clothing, and so quickly discard anything that is worn, that the federal government has reclassified sewing machines' place in economic growth measurements from the "apparel and upkeep" category to the "recreation" category.

Many of us accumulate so far beyond our needs that we cannot use nearly all of what we have. In those cases, we are spending more, but getting less, because the things we buy don't really serve our needs or purposes.

Other people go to the opposite extreme. Don't put off buying items that would have value to you every day merely to demonstrate your frugality, since the purpose of saving is to allow you to buy what you need.

Anticipating and accumulating consumer goods can contribute to a sense of personal well-being; however, placing too much emphasis on material goods has a diminishing effect on happiness.

Oropesa 1995

56

Accomplish something every day.

Sometimes days fly by without anything standing out in your mind, without any tangible improvement. Every day make sure, no matter how small the effort, that you do something to make your dreams come true.

☺ ☺ ☺

We've all heard the proverb "A journey of a thousand miles begins with a single step." But that same journey is vastly easier to make if the scenery changes.

If you keep moving and see different surroundings, you know you are making progress. If you can't see the progress you are making, if every step seems to leave you in the same place, then you will have trouble believing that you are moving forward.

Every day in your life you have to see the progress. Ask yourself, What did I accomplish today? If you have an answer, if you can see the progress you have made in your journey, then you have had a valuable day, a good day.

In research on hundreds of college students, individuals were found to be happiest when they felt they were moving closer to achieving their goals. Students who could not see progress were three times less likely to feel satisfied than students who could.

McGregor and Little 1998

57

Be flexible.

When we want to be with friends and family, often we want it to be on our terms. If everybody approaches relationships this way, no one will be happy. Instead of thinking only about what you want, think about what the others want too, and consider why it is important to spend time together. Accept that there are always differences between people and that if you are flexible you will enjoy your time with them more and feel closer to them.

Three sisters, Donna, Marie, and April, all want to hold the family's Christmas celebration at their house. For years, they took turns, rotating to all three houses every three years. Then Donna had a child and wanted to have the family over to her house every year. She wanted her son to be able to wake up and see the tree and spend the whole day at home. Marie didn't think that was fair. She wanted things done the same as they had always been done. Marie became uncomfortable at Donna's house, and Donna became uncomfortable at Marie's. April was left in the uncomfortable position of not being able to do anything except sacrifice her own turn.

Ultimately, the conflict existed because the sisters wanted to be together as a family. However, their desire to be together on their own terms kept them from being peacefully together. It is far better to be flexible enough to sacrifice what's personally ideal to have something acceptable, than to sacrifice the acceptable to have nothing.

Nearly all individuals report significant changes in their lives and in their values over the course of time. Those who viewed these changes as inevitable and remained open to the possibility that changes would be positive were 35 percent more likely to be satisfied with their lives than those who did not.

Minetti 1997

58

Events are temporary.

Bad things happen, but usually we do not feel their effects on us forever. It's really true that time heals wounds. Your disappointments are important and serious, but your distress will pass and your life will take you in new directions. Give yourself some time.

☺   ☺   ☺

The day after Dan lost his election to be mayor of his hometown, he felt like a load of bricks had dropped on him. He felt that he was a failure.

Almost thirty years later, Dan was asked about the things that defined him. Was the disappointment that had once sickened him first in his mind? No. His relationship with his wife, his life as a father, his commitment to political progress—these were the things he mentioned. Did he feel like a failure? Not at all. "Life is not wins and losses; it's how you live every day."

Studies of thousands of Americans show that happy people are not immune to negative events. Instead, they are characterized by the ability to think about other things in the aftermath of negative events.

Bless, Clore, Schwarz, and Golisano 1996

59

Be your own fan.

We need self-reinforcement, a belief in ourselves that is strong and unwavering. Be ready to pick yourself up when you are feeling down.

The young man walked up to his high school gym. A paper tacked to the wall listed the players who had made the varsity team.

Fifteen-year-old Michael Jordan looked up and down the list. He could not find his name. Michael Jordan had not made the team.

Michael Jordan is considered by most experts to be the best basketball player ever. But he had to believe in himself to get there. By the time many basketball players reach the tenth grade, they are receiving hundreds of letters from college coaches seeking to recruit them into their programs. Michael Jordan didn't receive a single letter, because Michael Jordan didn't make the team.

Michael Jordan didn't give up. He believed in himself and in his ability, and he practiced and practiced. The next year he made the team. And he became its star.

Rejection spells failure only if you do not believe in yourself. For those who believe, it is only a challenge.

The tendency to reinforce one's own self-confidence improves life satisfaction by about 20 percent for both men and women.

Seybolt and Wagner 1997

60

Join a group.

Take an inventory of your interests. Chances are there is a group in your area dedicated to your special interest. People in groups develop positive personal relationships that tend to make them feel more comfortable around others, less lonely, and more in control of events.

☺ ☺ ☺

Bob is an old-fashioned guy whose hobby is woodworking. Bob, who lives in rural Iowa, had retired and was looking for people who shared his interest.

He found himself involved with a woodworking group where he could pick up tips, exchange ideas, and correspond with people who shared his interest. Soon Bob was receiving messages from people all over the country who wanted to discuss their hobby, and he made a number of friendships.

When Bob's wife became seriously ill, he told his woodworking friends that he would be busy caring for his wife. Woodworking friends Bob had corresponded with were saddened and began discussing a project to make a get-well gift for Bob and his wife. Eventually twelve different people from across the country, including a policeman, a lawyer, an engineer, and a janitor, started working on pieces of a bookshelf.

The finished project was assembled by one of the group's members, and it was sent to Bob in Iowa.

Bob was touched by the gift. He could not believe the goodwill of his fellow woodworkers, and he was grateful that he had been a part of such a wonderful group.

Group membership tends to make people feel more connected to each other and increases personal confidence and satisfaction by 7 percent.

Coghlan 1989

61

Be positive.

Whether you are at home, in the workplace, or among friends, be the person who exudes optimism, and you will find it reflected right back at you.

☺ ☺ ☺

If you had a challenge ahead of you—whether you were trying to climb a mountain or just finish a project at work—what kind of people would you want to be surrounded with? Pessimistic people who reminded you why you were likely to fail, or optimistic people who gave you reasons you would succeed?

Think of the people you like to be around. Think of the people who are a joy to be around. What do they have in common? Are any of them pessimistic—continually expecting the worst to happen? No. We gravitate to people who approach life with pleasant expectations.

Living a satisfied life is one of the defining challenges of our life, and it is a challenge best met with optimism.

Scientists have a very hard time predicting a person's happiness based on the events he or she has experienced. Instead, a far better predictor of happiness than the number of good or bad events a person has endured are the beliefs and attitudes he or she maintains.

Chen 1996

62

There will be an end,
but you can be prepared.

One of the great sources of anxiety as we age is that we will never get a chance to do that thing we always wanted to do, or to finish that project we were working on years ago, or to mend the fences that may have fallen into disrepair as our relationships evolved. Don't wait until the end of your life to figure out what you wished you had done. Think of those things now and do them.

Students often will procrastinate. Assign them a paper, with two months to do it, and many will literally wait until the last day, cramming through their readings, making notes, and then charging through the writing. Not a moment of this process is enjoyed. It is a manic effort, with little concern for quality. Students who write their papers in a timely fashion, anticipate what needs to be done, and do the work in an orderly process never feel out of control, and can even enjoy themselves.

We live life like a student writing a paper—either as the procrastinator or the planner. The procrastinator feels out of control, and each passing year is a source of desperation. The planner finishes what needs to be done, and treats each passing year as a sign of accomplishment.

Research on senior citizens finds that those who are most comfortable with their own mortality do not ignore the matter, but prepare themselves for it.

Oates 1997

63

How we see the world is more important than how the world is.

What is the shape of the world, what condition is it in? Scientists, philosophers, and kings could offer a never-ending debate on the question. But there is no real grade for the world apart from the one you assign it.

☺   ☺   ☺

Scientists did a study in which they showed people a deck of playing cards. On each of these cards, however, something was wrong, something differed from the usual. The four of clubs was red, the five of diamonds had six diamonds. People were shown the cards and asked what they saw.

Were people surprised to see these obviously error-filled cards? They were not, because they didn't notice. When asked to describe the cards they were looking at, people answered they were looking at the five of diamonds or the four of clubs. They didn't mention that the cards were mismarked.

Why did this happen? Because what we see is a function not only of what is really there, but also of what we are looking for—our expectations, our assumptions.

People who have experienced similar life events can wind up with nearly opposite perceptions of life satisfaction. Researchers have compared, for example, people who have received a job promotion, and they found that while some of the people treasure the opportunity others lament the added responsibility. The implications of life events are a matter of perspective.

Chen 1996

64

Keep a pen and paper handy.

People often feel frustrated that they can't remember a good idea they had last week or an interesting dream they had last night. Those who keep a notebook feel like they are more in control and are missing less.

☺ ☺ ☺

Emily is an aspiring writer and is always writing things down. Even when she can't find paper, she scrambles to find envelopes, napkins, a piece of cardboard, anything that she can use to write down her thoughts. Does she do this because she is a particularly forgetful person? No, it is because she is both realistic enough and disciplined enough to know that human beings run across too many ideas in a day to remember all of them or even most of them. Good ideas come floating into our heads and will just as easily float right out. Writers who acknowledge this carry around a notebook so that the best of those ideas make it to paper. You don't have to be a writer, however, to have good ideas floating through you. Keep a notebook and pen handy, and you will be able to hold onto those fleeting thoughts.

While purposeful activity contributes to happiness, feelings of lost thoughts and opportunities contribute to an unhealthy frustration. People who feel like their best ideas escape them are 37 percent less likely to feel content than people who do not.

Madigan, Mise, and Maynard 1996

65

Help the next person
who needs some minor assistance.

Giving help is a win-win situation, so take the time to pay attention
to your surroundings and offer the help that you can. It could be as
simple as making a habit of holding the door open for the person
coming in behind you. It's a gesture of friendliness that makes
another person feel better and makes you feel good about yourself.

☺   ☺   ☺

Stacy moved to the Midwest from the Northeast and quickly
noticed that people in the Midwest seemed to be in the habit of
being courteous drivers. If you were stuck trying to get out of a
parking lot, with a mile-long procession of cars in front of you
on the main road, people in the Midwest would stop and give
you room to pull out.

Based on their example, Stacy got in the habit of letting cars
out when traffic was backed up. Stacy liked this friendly
approach to life and soon received a dramatic example of its
value.

After letting a car out in front of her, Stacy soon had to pull
over to the side of the road because her car was making a
strange noise. The driver she had let out saw her pull over and

followed her. The other driver asked Stacy if she needed any help, and after a brief investigation concluded that Stacy had just run out of gas. He gave her enough gas to get her to a station and told her how nice he found people in this part of the country. She gave him her telephone number, and one year later they were married.

Life satisfaction was found to improve 24 percent with the level of altruistic activity.

Williams, Haber, Weaver, and Freeman 1998

66

Take care not to harshly criticize family and friends.

We rely on those closest to us for support. We can accept critical words from those who are not close to us because we can believe they reflect a lack of knowledge about us rather than an actual flaw in us. From our friends and family, however, critical words cut deeply. Try to avoid fixing your friends and family. Love them for who they are. If you must say something negative, always be constructive. Make your criticism reflect your love and respect, not your disappointment.

☺   ☺   ☺

"Well, that was stupid," Carol's mother said to her as Carol explained how she had lost a file at work and in the process made her boss angry at her. *Stupid.* The word flew out of her mother's mouth and slapped Carol in the head. She didn't like having her boss disappointed with her, but her own mother calling her stupid was painful.

Stupid is a common word, with a range of meanings from ill-considered to ignorant. Maybe Carol's mother meant it in the nicest possible terms, but even then, when speaking to someone, especially someone close, you have to assume that your words will be taken in the strongest, least positive way.

Aggression and fixations on disagreements reduces satisfaction in relationships by nearly 70 percent.

Chand 1990

67

Some people like the big picture, and others like the details.

When you look at a restaurant bill, you can eye the total due or you can focus on each item listed. Life is the same way. You can think in terms of the totality of what you have accomplished, or you can think in terms of the momentary episodes of your life. Adopt the focus that makes you feel more satisfied. If you think things turned out all right even though there were bumps in the road, think big picture. If you're not sure how it will turn out but you know that your life has been marked with moments of great happiness and pleasure, then focus on the details.

It's Saturday afternoon, and two men who live next door to each other in older homes of about the same size and condition are in their backyards. One is swinging in a hammock. The other is sweating in the sun, painting his fence. The man in the hammock is happy and comfortable knowing that his house will stand for many, many years, offering him and his family shelter. His neighbor is happy, too, because he is thinking about how sharp the fence will look with a little paint, and he takes satisfaction from how good the backdoor looks that he painted last week. One is taking comfort in the big picture, the other in the details. The important thing is that they find satisfaction.

Researchers find that it is not more typical to experience happiness as following from events or to experience our perspective on events as flowing from happiness; both patterns are prevalent.

Scherpenzeel and Saris 1996

68

Do things you are good at.

We need to feel competent. Take on responsibilities in areas in which you excel, whether it's cooking, gardening, or accounting, and ask for help when you are struggling.

☺ ☺ ☺

Researchers at Penn State noticed a rather pronounced trend in students' grades. In departments where students have fewer required courses, the students receive generally higher grades. At first the researchers assumed this was because those students took the easiest classes available. Then they found those students had higher grades in both their electives and their required classes.

The researchers concluded the root of this pattern was that by having more freedom to choose classes, students indeed tended to take courses they were interested in and that they could do well in. But, more important, doing well in those elective classes actually improved their performance in all their classes, because the positive habits that success created in the electives carried over into their required courses.

Who is happier, stay-at-home parents or parents who work outside the home? In studies comparing members of those two groups, researchers found happiness in both situations if the person felt competent at what they were doing.

Haw 1995

69

Go visit your neighbor.

We no longer live in a time when people know all their neighbors and consider them to be friends. A shocking number of people have never had a conversation with their neighbors, and some couldn't pick them out of a lineup. Introduce yourself, or invite your neighbor over for coffee. Neighbors are not only a great potential source of friendship, they make us feel more comfortable in our homes, which is where most of us spend much of our time.

New houses are being built across the country with an amazing new feature: front porches. According to the National Association of Home Builders, space that once might have been dedicated to a living room is now more likely to be used for a front porch.

Architects, builders, and town planners see the front porch as one remedy to the unhappy and uncomfortable social distance that characterizes many neighborhoods. Many of us don't know who our neighbors are, and often we don't know anything about them. This despite the fact that we have something tremendously important in common—our neighborhood, our surroundings, the place we begin and end each day. Front porches are making a comeback because most of us would like the chance to venture outside our front door and meet the people on our street.

☺   ☺   ☺

Greater community interactions can increase happiness by almost 30 percent.

Sugarman 1997

70

Smile.

Your smile makes other people happy, which in turn makes you happy.

☺ ☺ ☺

If you could do something that would make people happy, and it would cost you neither money nor time, would you do it? If that same thing also made you happy, would you do it? What is this magical thing that will brighten your day and the days of people around you and yet cost you nothing? A smile.

Scientists at the University of California in San Francisco have identified nineteen different kinds of smiles, each of them capable of communicating a pleasant message that will often be met with a smile in return.

☺ ☺ ☺

In a study of adults of various ages, a tendency was found for subjects to mimic the expressions of those around them. In other words, sad faces evoked more sad faces, and smiling faces evoked smiles and happiness.

Lundqvist and Dimberg 1995

71

Don't accept television's picture of the world.

Watch television for any length of time, whether it's the news or a prime-time show, and you will inevitably come to the conclusion that virtually everyone is either very rich or about to die a horrible, bloody death. These pictures affect us more than we know. We fear that the awful events on television will happen to us, and we are frustrated that the nearly universal wealth we see on television hasn't reached us yet. Separate what you see from what you know to be real. Base your expectations on reality, not on television.

For a thousand generations, the Gwinch'in tribe lived in northern Alaska in nearly complete isolation from outside cultures. Tribal members were completely self-sufficient, surviving on skills taught to them by their parents and elders.

In 1980, one of the tribe's leaders acquired a television.

Members of the tribe describe the event as the beginning of an addiction. Soon the native customs were ignored to maximize TV-watching time. One researcher said of the tribe's experience, "For these natives, like anyone else, television is a cultural nerve gas. It's odorless, painless and tasteless, and deadly."

What happened to the Gwinch'in traditions that had existed for thousands of years? In the words of one tribe member, "Television made us wish we were something else. It taught us greed and waste, and now everything that we were is gone."

Television changes our view of the world, and can encourage us to develop highly unrealistic and often damaging conclusions that serve to reduce our life satisfaction by up to 50 percent.

Jeffres and Dobos 1995

72

You always have a choice.

Remember, you don't have to do anything. You can choose to do whatever you think is important enough to warrant your efforts. Don't lament your responsibilities as burdensome and unavoidable. Think of the positive effects of your actions—the reasons you go to work, the reasons you keep the household running.

How many times have you complained to yourself, "Why do I have to do this?" Would you believe that you don't have to do it? Unless you are in prison, you don't have to do anything. You choose to do things.

You might ask, "What difference does that make? I have to do the laundry, or I choose to do the laundry. Either way it has to be done."

It makes a tremendous difference. It is the difference between taking an action because something of value is at stake for you, and taking an action because you are being forced to do so. Doing the laundry is a choice you make because you value being clean and presentable, or you do the laundry for your family members because you love them.

Every time we do the laundry we are doing it because we want to. Is anyone forcing you to do the laundry? No. When you see all the options you have, you can begin to appreciate the choices you make.

Interviews on life satisfaction levels found that those who expressed a sense of autonomy, of making decisions for themselves, were three times more likely to feel satisfied than those who did not.

Fisher 1995

73

Be agreeable.

Make it easy for people to deal with you. Don't be angry or disruptive merely because you can.

Saturday morning, Frank went to play golf with his friend Mark. He told his wife, Michelle, that he'd be home around two. After golf, Mark asked Frank to help him move some furniture back at his place. After the furniture was moved, Mark offered Frank a sandwich, and soon the afternoon was slipping away. Frank looked at his watch as he drove home and was startled to see that it was after five. He hadn't called Michelle. He had said he'd be home hours ago, and he hadn't called. She was going to be mad. She probably had made some plans, and now he was hours late, and he hadn't called. This could easily turn into an argument, then the whole night would be shot.

Frank walked through the door thinking of possible excuses, but instead he apologized and offered to make dinner. Michelle smiled, accepted his offer, and asked him how his day was. And they both happily enjoyed their evening.

Researchers found that having a positive attitude about those around us is among the most important predictors of life satisfaction and that without such attitudes, we are less than half as likely to feel happy.

Glass and Jolly 1997

74

Don't ignore one part of your life.

We are happier when all the pieces of our life are generally in good shape than when one area we care about is perfect and everything else is falling apart.

Notice the way some organizations make decisions. They make them in separate units rather than thinking about the organization as a whole.

A university will assign a first-floor classroom for an early morning final exam despite the fact that the maintenance crew is at that very same time cutting the grass right outside the window. Why? The classroom was chosen by the dean because it was precisely the right size, while the maintenance workers were sent out by their manager because it's cooler in the mornings and therefore easier to work outside.

What's the result? The two tasks conflict with each other, and neither will be a success. The exam is disrupted by the noise, and ultimately the lawn cutting is stopped before it's finished to suit the needs of the students.

You have an advantage over an organization, though. You know about all your needs and priorities. Your task is to take all of them into account as you pursue your goals.

In research on a large group of college students, those who were less likely to link the attainment of a specific goal to their overall mood were 19 percent more likely to be satisfied.

Smith 1997

75

Listen to music.

Music communicates to us on many different levels, and our favorite music tends to transport our mind to its favorite place.

☺ ☺ ☺

Do you know what happened when professors played Mozart to their classes while the students worked on a series of tests? The students did better. Why? Because scientists have found that music stimulates our brain.

Contrary to some reports that have suggested this effect occurs mainly with infants, the actual research suggests music has positive effects for any age. Music excites our mind, whether we are one, forty-one, or a hundred and one.

☺ ☺ ☺

A positive effect on mood was found for 92 percent of individuals when they listened to the music of their choice. Excitement and happiness were typical reactions to the music.

Hakanen 1995

76

Let your goals guide you.

When you have chosen reasonable, meaningful, and aligned goals, pursue them with all your heart.

☺   ☺   ☺

Imagine yourself in your kitchen, about to make something tremendous. Do you spend hours taking every product in your cabinet and every food in your refrigerator, pouring it all in one giant bowl, mixing it, baking it, and then putting it on your table? No doubt, even if you went to great effort at great expense, you would wind up with a giant inedible pile of garbage.

What if, instead, you carefully followed a recipe, went to the store to buy just what you needed, put in just the right amount of the perfect ingredients, and cooked it as instructed? Then you would wind up with exactly what you wanted.

Life works the same way. It doesn't take everything you have, and everything you can get your hands on, to wind up where you want to be. It takes a plan and the patience to follow the needed steps.

In ongoing interviews with a group of attorneys, a distinct transition was noted as career became less important and family more important. Those who recognized the change and reorganized their priorities accordingly expressed 29 percent more life satisfaction than those who did not.

Adams 1983

77

Use your job positively.

At its best, work gives us a sense of purpose and enhances our appreciation of our life outside of the workplace. Appreciate all that your job gives you, and it will help you appreciate what really matters.

☺   ☺   ☺

Wisconsin has a new program that tries to place all the unemployed people in the state into jobs. Do you know what the people who get jobs like the most after they find themselves employed? It's not the money. It's the self-respect. They see their job as a chance to demonstrate their responsibility, their ability, their dependability, and they find that working makes all those things clear, not just to others but to themselves. Use your job, not as a sentence, not as punishment, but as a chance to show off—and show yourself—what you can do.

☺   ☺   ☺

Research on over 1,500 mothers found that working outside the home increased life satisfaction 5 percent and contributed to a feeling of equality in the family.

Rogers 1996

78

Don't forget to have fun.

Every day leave yourself some time to enjoy, to be silly, to laugh.

☺ ☺ ☺

Watch children running around in the playground and you will soon be thinking, "They're having so much fun." Why are *they* having so much fun? The better question is, Why aren't *you* having more fun? Children run around and play as if by instinct. They do not question whether they should have fun, they just go out and do it. Adults have responsibilities, we are serious. Ask one of your friends to do something fun with you, and you might hear, "I don't have time for that." Imagine a child being asked if she wanted to go to the zoo and answering, "I'll have to get back to you, I'm really swamped right now." Sometimes children know better than we do. Having a little fun, a time for pure silliness and happiness, is an essential part of every day.

Regularly having fun is one of the five central factors in leading a satisfied life. Individuals who spend time just having fun are 20 percent more likely to feel happy on a daily basis and 36 percent more likely to feel comfortable with their age and stage in life.

Lepper 1996

79

Believe in ultimate justice.

That there are many problems in the world is obvious to anyone, but take comfort in the notion that eventually good prevails. Whether your focus is on the criminal justice system or a spiritual system, realize that those who have wronged the world will eventually pay some price.

John List was a mild-mannered, unremarkable-looking older man. The kind you saw on the street and didn't give a second thought to. One day a television show did a story on John List. Decades earlier, this unremarkable man had committed a heinous crime, murdering his family. He assumed another life and hid from his crime for decades.

Did he "get away with it" all those years? Well, he certainly wasn't in prison, but he later described the personal hell of waiting every moment for the mask to be broken and for his new world to crumble.

Regardless of the experiences subjects personally dealt with, whether they had personally been the victim of a crime or known someone close who had, those who believed the world is ultimately just retained a 13 percent higher level of life satisfaction.

Lipkus, Dalbert, and Siegler 1996

80

Reminisce.

Think of the happy times you, your family, and friends have had together. Recalling happiness of the past has the powerful ability to bring us happiness in the present.

Neil came over on a boat when he was fourteen years old. He came by himself to a new country where he didn't know anyone. He got a job as a handyman, working for the mayor of a small East Coast city. It was an old-time political machine, and the mayor seemed to run everything in town. Neil would tell his grandchildren story after story about his trip to America and his early years working for the mayor.

This was his favorite story: Neil was walking across town in a frayed suit from the thrift shop that was two sizes too small. The mayor saw Neil walking by and asked him where he was going. Neil said he was on his way to the church, he was about to be married. The mayor looked him up and down and said he should have a proper suit to be married in. Neil was embarrassed and told the mayor he did not have enough money to buy new clothes. The mayor told Neil that today he would be the best-dressed man in the city, and he quickly whisked him off to the tailor. The tailor's shop was closed. The mayor sent the police to find the tailor, who came in because the mayor asked him. The tailor made a fine set of clothes for Neil and asked Neil for no money.

Neil never grew tired of recounting his pride and excitement from that day—that the mayor had showed him such kindness and that he had not been a disappointment to his bride. No matter how many times Neil told the story, it brought him a warm feeling inside.

When people consciously choose to think back on their past, over 80 percent tend to focus on very positive memories.

Hogstel and Curry 1995

81

Be conscientious.

Finish what you start. Care about what you are doing, and do it right. Although being conscientious is not as easy as slacking off, we feel better about ourselves when we do a good job.

☺ ☺ ☺

Locals love to tell the story of the bridge to nowhere. In southwest Florida, engineers had designed one of the biggest bridges in the state. The bridge was so big that they had to build it by starting on both banks and building toward the center. Trouble is, when they reached the middle, the two sides didn't meet. They were two feet apart. Millions upon millions of dollars, and thousands upon thousands of worker-hours, and the whole thing didn't work. You know what they did? They built a second new bridge.

It's an old saying, but it still applies. There are two ways to do something: take some time and do it right, or hurry the job and never finish.

Research on adults reveals that a tendency to be disciplined, deliberate, and dutiful has an 18 percent positive effect on happiness.

Furnham and Cheng 1997

82

Don't dwell on unwinnable conflicts.

Move on. The problems you spend your time and energy on should be both important and improvable. Otherwise, you are better off moving on to things you can change.

In mythology, Sisyphus was doomed to the endless task of pushing a boulder up a hill. Just before he got it to the top he would lose his hold, and the boulder would roll back down to the bottom. Sisyphus would push the boulder up again and almost have it to the top before it fell back. There was, of course, no point. It was just a death sentence.

Some of us approach our disagreements and disappointments as if they were Sisyphus's boulder. We push and push and push and never consider that there is no point. The beauty of real life, though, is that our boulders are of our own creation and will disappear if we just stop pushing.

Many people experience conflict in balancing their time between work and home. Studies find that people who want to spend more time in both settings wind up feeling decreased satisfaction at home and at work. Those who recognize that their limited time is a conflict without a readily available solution are one-fourth more likely to feel comfortable with themselves than those who do not.

Caproni 1997

83

Enjoy the ordinary.

You do countless things in the average day that can be labeled as chores or can be relabeled as enjoyable. Walking the dog is something that has to be done, yes, but while you walk the dog you get some pleasant exercise, some time to think, and a chance to see the neighbors and the neighborhood. Enjoy what you do every day.

We know most days will be regular days. Our lives will include some highlight days that stay with us forever, like family celebrations or personal triumphs, but almost every day this year will be a regular day, with nothing particularly astounding about it.

Yet within these regular days are many opportunities for enjoyment, many of which we don't even think about or really appreciate. Take a moment every day to think about the simple pleasures of your daily life.

Take Lonnie, for example, who recently enjoyed his 103rd birthday. Lonnie sat in a rocking chair on his front porch, gently rocking back and forth as reporters asked him how he felt on this special day. He said he felt great because every day was special to him.

☺   ☺   ☺

In a study of over thirteen-thousand people, 96 percent of subjects rated their satisfaction with life typically no higher than
"fairly positive." The satisfied life was not one of extremes but of
steady, generally positive feelings.

Diener and Diener 1995

84

Focus not on the world's tragedies, but on the world's hope.

Many sad things happen in our world, but rather than focusing on them, have hope for the future. Think of the world's potential. Perhaps the future holds the curing of diseases, the end of violence, the amelioration of poverty and hunger.

The San Jacinto Girl Scout Council wanted to do something fun, exciting, and uniting in their community. They decided to try to create the world's largest friendship circle, a circle of people holding hands in a celebration of community.

The Girl Scouts invited local residents to join them, and on a Saturday morning at a nearby amusement park, they set up their circle. The mayor of Houston as well as 6,243 other people participated in the event. The circle stretched out for over a mile, as people joined hands to celebrate the group's message that "friendship conquers hatred." One Girl Scout leader said the day's events were meant to "teach girls and adults that everybody matters, and to value differences among ourselves."

As a nine-year-old scout explained, "It's important to be a friend to everybody because you could hurt somebody's feelings."

Over nine in ten Americans are uncomfortable or worried about aspects of the world and of society. The difference between more and less happy people is what they do with that discomfort. Less happy people wallow in the problems they see, while happier people focus on potential improvements in the future.

Garrett 1996

85

Get a hobby.

Hobbies are a steady source of interest, providing two essential ingredients in life: consistency and fun.

☺   ☺   ☺

Elsa collects old books. She has all sorts of books lining the shelves of her home, some classics, some rare first editions, and some she just likes to page through. For Elsa, collecting books is a source of entertainment and a source of connection to all sorts of people she meets. Every town she visits is a potential source of adventure as she visits antique shops and used bookstores, looking to add to her collection. What does collecting books mean to Elsa? "It puts me in touch with history, it puts me in touch with other people who I meet and trade books with, and most important, I just like having books around."

☺   ☺   ☺

In surveys of thousands of adults, those who had a hobby were found to be 6 percent more likely to rate their lives favorably.

Mookherjee 1997

86

Envying other people's relationships
is pointless.

People with many friends sometimes yearn for a closer family, and people with a close family sometimes yearn for more friends. The key to continued satisfaction with life is not in replicating what someone else has. Instead, build a support system that you draw from and give to, regardless of whether it is made up primarily of friends or family.

A group of philosophers and historians gathered a few years back to study the advantages of family life two centuries ago. They were concerned about the instability in our current family situations and the widespread fear that our society is suffering from the lack of traditional family relationships. The academics wondered if the agrarian family unit—a stable mother-father bond and a large group of siblings—was really ideal for humans and if any of the lessons from yesteryear could be applied today.

Here's what they concluded: today we envy the traditional family for its cohesion and stability, while two hundred years ago members of the traditional family often felt that their individuality was overwhelmed by their family unit—that they were not really a full person, just a cog in the family machine.

The irony of this situation was not lost on the researchers. Today many of us yearn for more contact with our family, while two hundred years ago people had so much contact with their families that they became sick of one another. The best hope is to enjoy the relationships you have, neither forcing them to meet some artificial standard nor holding them up for comparison with anyone else's life and loves.

In research on over 8,000 adults, researchers considered over 100 factors that contribute to happiness. Among the factors that had a major negative effect was the use of comparisons that implied personal failures in relationships, which reduced happiness by 26 percent.

Li, Young, Wei, Zhang, Zheng, Xiao, Wang, and Chen 1998

87

Give yourself time to adapt to change.

Don't expect to be immediately comfortable after a move or in a new situation. Give yourself time to adjust. If you learn how to ease yourself into new circumstances, changes you make in the future will be easier for you.

☺ ☺ ☺

Jill is a respected veteran teacher, having taught eighth-graders for over twenty years. Teachers have a unique job in that each year they begin again and are surrounded by an entirely new cast of characters. Even though Jill was experienced and loved teaching, every year she had the same ritual the night before the first day of school. She tossed and turned, worried and wondered, and barely slept at all.

Jill acknowledges the human instinct to be uncomfortable with change and lets herself be nervous about meeting twenty-five new faces that first day. Soon, though, she takes comfort in the familiar aspects that remain constant, and she recharges with the notion that she is about to embark on a new adventure, unlike any she has taken before.

In a study of newly married couples, those couples who acknowledged the difficulties of their new situation were 1.5 times more comfortable with each other, and with marriage, than those who tried to conceal the difficulty of dealing with change.

Monteiro 1991

88

Focus on what really matters to you.

There is no point in competing in a game that you do not really care to win. Don't allow your life and expectations to become anything but deeply personal reflections of what matters the most to you.

☺   ☺   ☺

The 1999 winner of the Nathan's Hot Dog Eating Contest was accused of cheating. They say he started to eat his first hot dog before the twelve-minute time limit began. When time was up, he had consumed twenty and one-quarter hot dogs, while the second place finisher had eaten twenty. The matter is of great importance to the top two finishers. Each desperately wants to be the hot dog eating champion.

Would you enter a hot dog eating contest, which requires you to prepare by regularly eating unhealthy amounts of food in a short period of time? Probably not, because your hot dog eating abilities are not something you really pride yourself on, not something that really matters to you.

Yet many of us are constantly in competitions where we don't really want the prize. We find someone to be in a secret economic competition with—a friend, a neighbor, a loved one.

We size up their home, their car, their lifestyle and try to do them one better. But our life is not changed for the better if the engine falls out of their car or if they suddenly have to cancel a vacation because of finances. Others look around at work for a rival and measure their relative progress against the other person.

But is this really your goal? Were you born into this world to get promoted before one of your co-workers? Were you born into this world to get a better car than your neighbors? Let your real goals guide you, not meaningless competitions you don't really benefit by winning.

Goals are crucial to one's orientation to the world and to life satisfaction. If one's goals conform to one's self-concept, it increases by 43 percent the likelihood that goals will contribute in a positive fashion to life satisfaction.

Emmons and Kaiser 1996

89

Realize that complete satisfaction does not exist.

Set your sights on being generally satisfied and generally happy, not on expecting every aspect of life to be perfect. Complete satisfaction does not exist because everything can be improved upon. Those who accept this can appreciate what they have. Those who do not accept this can never appreciate what they have even as their circumstances improve. Strive to improve. Don't try to be perfect.

☺ ☺ ☺

"Golf," according to Mark Twain, "is a good walk spoiled." Golf is perhaps the most frustrating of all games. It seems so simple. A white ball—stationary, for goodness' sake! You swing a club, the ball flies, you walk to the ball, and you do it again. The problem with hitting a golf ball is that because it requires an almost infinite series of body contortions, club movements, and angles, it always results in a less than perfect shot.

If you listen to people who play golf for fun, you will hear them say, "Just let me get one birdie. Just one birdie, and I will be happy." A birdie is the score you get when you hit the ball in the hole in one less shot than it would take the average professional to do it. And do you know what happens when they get that first birdie? They say, "Just one more birdie." Every improvement in their game is inexorably followed by the demand for further improvement.

Golf equipment makers know that players are so desperate they will try to buy their way to improvement. As one manufacturer explained, "You'll never run out of things to sell a golfer. Golfers would buy a swing if they could, especially if it would let them hit the ball straight and toward the target every time."

But they can never, ever reach perfection. That's right, even professional golfers spend their entire careers hitting less than perfect shots.

Those who believe they will fail to achieve their goals are unhappy, but so too are those who believe they will exactly meet their goals. Those who are happiest believe they will meet some of their goals and will receive satisfaction from multiple aspects of their lives.

Chen 1996

90

Surround yourself with pleasant aromas.

Here's a simple way to make yourself feel better. Air out your house, and add some fragrant flowers. Make your home smell nice, and you will feel the effects.

Five hundred years ago, soldiers in Europe used good-smelling spices to distract the injured from their pain. Today, doctors are experimenting with aromatherapy in the hospital, using good smells to comfort those in postoperative recovery.

Bad smells are crafty characters. They get in our lives, and they never leave. If you live with them long enough, you can't even notice them, because they've been around too long. An old musty carpet or some other source of odor is really an attack on our senses. Not noticing the smell is not the same as the smell not being there. We've just surrendered our sense of smell and our brain, unwilling to continue processing something so unpleasant.

Good smells, on the other hand, as soldiers knew in the fifteenth century, and doctors are rediscovering today, awaken the senses and the brain and at a subconscious level remind us of good things.

Our senses operate all the time, offering us important signals about our environment. Pleasant smells evoke surprise and happiness for more than eight out of ten individuals, while unpleasant odors trigger disgust and unhappy reactions.

Alaoui-Ismaieli, Robin, Rada, Dittmar, and Vernet-Maury 1997

91

Don't let others set your goals.

Too many people choose goals based on what others think. Instead, think about what you really care about, and set meaningful goals to accomplish what matters to you.

Gary left the military after twenty years of service as a marine pilot. His military friends were surprised that he would leave with the possibility of promotion dangling in front of him. How could he do this? What was wrong with him? His friends didn't quite say this to him, but that is what they wanted to know.

Gary had an answer. "Holding the highest rank has never been my dream," he said. "It might be your dream, and that's fine, but it isn't mine."

Gary's dream was to serve his country by serving children. He offered his services to the local school district, and in a matter of a few years was asked to run a new and rigorous high school academic program. Learning, according to Gary, is a lot like flying. "You have your hands on the controls, you have the power to excel. It's all within your hands." Teaching is, for him, a dream come true, a dream that could never have come true if Gary had worried about what other people thought he should do.

People do not have to succeed in absolutely everything they do to feel happy. But, people do have to believe they have maintained control over their own life. In fact, those who feel that they were responsible for their own position and decisions express one-third more life satisfaction than those who do not.

Kean, Van Zandt, and Miller 1996

92

You are a person, not a stereotype.

People are happiest when they allow their individual personality to come out, not when they conform to popular images. Men who believe they must act tough and women who believe they must act soft are boxed in to a set of expectations that have nothing to do with who they are.

Look around at a funeral, and you will see women crying and men standing with steely faces. Men have been taught to be tough, not to reveal their emotions. Women have been taught to be more open, more expressive. The National Institutes of Health has documented that with both physical and emotional pain, men are much less likely than women to reveal their discomfort.

It is important to remember, though, that not all of us fit those expectations.

A man who wants to cry at a funeral but stops himself because he's been taught to be tough is not really being tough. He's pretending to be what he thinks people expect of him. A woman who forces herself to open up in front of others but who would rather act more reserved is not a nicer person for showing her emotions and will not be happier for having to act in a way that is unnatural to her.

You have to act the way you think is appropriate, not the way you think the average man or woman is supposed to act. Our generalizations about men and women are often false and too often damaging.

Satisfaction with life was not found to be connected to how well men and women fit into gender stereotypes of femininity and masculinity.

Ramanaiah, Detwiler, and Byravan 1995

93

Know what makes you happy and sad.

People feel worse if they are unhappy but have no idea why. Think about your feelings and emotions. Then, even when you are unhappy, you will take comfort in knowing the cause and how it can be changed.

☺   ☺   ☺

Professor John Hamler teaches a course on scientific thinking. He demystifies science on the first day of the class with the first words he says: "All science is noticing patterns."

He explains to his students that scientists see the world in a very orderly way. They look for what goes with what. Events and conditions are not random; they have causes and effect. "Science is noticing patterns, great and small. What happens when you throw a rock up in the air? It comes back down every time. That is a pattern; that is the essence of science."

The difference between most people and scientists, Professor Hamler explains, "is that people let the world be random to them. They allow events to pass without connecting them to other events. Whatever happens, it just happens, there's nothing else to it. Scientists everywhere, all the time, see connections because they are looking for connections."

In dealing with our own emotions and life satisfaction, we need to be scientists. We need to notice patterns. Those who let themselves exist in the midst of random events not only don't understand what is happening to them, they also can't do anything to change their world.

Those who are least likely to quickly overcome a temporary sense of dissatisfaction with life are those who cannot define the sources of their feelings.

Ramanaiah and Detwiler 1997

94

Keep reading.

Those who read books benefit from what they learn and the entertainment they receive. But in addition, they get to exercise their brain, and when we do that, we feel satisfied that we are spending our time wisely.

☺ ☺ ☺

Which would you choose to be, a person with an ever-decreasing attention span, or a person with an ever-increasing attention span? A person with access to the second- and third-rate work that would have been considered trash two decades ago, or a person with access to the work of the greatest minds we have ever known? A person with access to a perpetual run of the same basic story with the same basic characters, or a person with access to an array of choices that span nearly an infinite imagination? A person who likely won't be able to remember a story ten minutes later, or a person who might carry a tale for the rest of his or her life?

Which would you rather be, a person who usually spends his or her free time in front of the television, or a person who usually spends his or her free time reading?

Reading engages the mind. Reading materials, by exercising our memory and imagination, can contribute to happiness in ways similar to active positive thinking. Regular readers are about 8 percent more likely to express daily satisfaction.

Scope 1999

95

We must feel needed.

Think of those who rely on your friendship, caring, guidance, help. You probably don't realize how important you are to the people in your life.

☺ ☺ ☺

The Labor Department has done a study on older workers to find out what keeps them coming to work and what encourages them to retire. One of the most often cited reasons for stopping work is not that they are tired or want to spend more time in their garden. What often sends older folks into retirement is the feeling that they are no longer needed on the job. Workers retired when they felt that their purpose was in doubt, that others could do what they could do better, and that they were only taking up space. They left because they were no longer needed.

Think about what this means for our personal lives. Even though we can't retire from our personal lives, we still need to feel needed. Remember how much other people matter to you, and realize that you matter to them just as much.

In an experimental research program, a relationship was found between happiness and helping behavior. By helping others, we create positive bonds with people and enhance our self image. Those who had more opportunities to offer help felt 11 percent better about themselves.

Pegalis 1994

96

Say "so what."

A classmate at your high school reunion is richer, prettier, smarter, than everybody else. Does it matter? No. Your life is shaped more by your everyday relationships than by the lives of acquaintances you see only rarely.

☺   ☺   ☺

Two friends from high school, Ken and Alan, went off to college and on to separate careers. Alan became a social worker, helping distressed families. Ken became a computer consultant, founded his own company, and became super-rich.

Alan loved his job and felt great about the impact he was able to make on the families he worked with. But with Ken in the news—newspapers covering his company's success and his growing fortune—Alan began to question his choices.

How could someone he know be so rich while he lived such a modest life? Why didn't he have Ken's success?

The truth is, Alan didn't *want* Ken's success. He was never interested in dedicating his life to a corporation, and he didn't spend his days dreaming of riches. He wanted to help people, and he was helping people. His jealousy of Ken's life faded away as he looked at the smiling faces of the children he helped every day.

Sometimes we look at what other people have and we want that instead of thinking about what really and truly motivates us, what we really and truly want and need. Don't take someone else's accomplishment as evidence that you are doing anything wrong.

Satisfaction with life was found to be related to experiences with family and friends—those with regular participation in one's life—and to be unrelated to those with whom contact is brief or irregular.

Hong and Duff 1997

97

Have a purpose.

Without a purpose nothing matters. You can work forty hours a week, come home to cook, clean, and then take up seventy-two new good habits, but if there isn't a reason you are doing it, none of these activities will mean anything to you.

☺ ☺ ☺

Say you're a student. Why should you study for a test? To do well in the course. Why do you care if you do well in the course? So you can get a degree. Why do you care if you get a degree? Because it will help you get a good job. Now, the job may be years away, but it is the foundation upon which all your efforts are based. Take away the eventual outcome, and all the steps in between become just killing time. Why bother doing any of these things if they are not leading toward something you care about? It's more fun to goof off than study for the test, and if there is nothing at stake, then we goof off.

It is much easier to apply yourself to the activities you do for your family or your personal success if you define what you want and are able to see how what you are doing is leading you forward.

In research on college students, a comparison was made between students who enjoyed their lives and studies and students who were least comfortable with their environment. A major difference between the two groups was a sense of underlying purpose in life, which almost twice as many of the former group had.

Rahman and Khaleque 1996

98

You have not finished the best part of your life.

We hear that youth is wasted on the young. People who say this are accepting the myth that only the young can enjoy life to the fullest. The truth is that older people do not consider their young days to be their best days; most enjoy their senior years more than any other part of their life.

☺ ☺ ☺

Warren was a middle-aged professor. Comfortable in all respects, he anticipated that he would continue teaching for many years. The college faced a budget shortfall, however, and took the unprecedented step of eliminating a number of its academic departments, including Warren's.

For Warren, everything seemed to have been destroyed. Everything he counted on was gone, and he felt too old to start all over again. Too old to search for another college to employ him, and too old to restart his life.

Instead of giving up, Warren realized how much the world had to offer. Instead of concluding that he had suffered a loss that could never be replaced, he chose to focus on the opportunity set before him. Never before had he had the chance to start again, to decide what he wanted to do and where he wanted to do it.

He wound up taking a year off from the world to live in a rural town. And how did he feel at the end of the year? "I've never been better."

Researchers conducted a long-term study of northern Californians, interviewing subjects multiple times over three decades. When asked when they had been the happiest in their lives, each time eight out of ten answered "right now."

Field 1997

99

Money does not buy happiness.

We spend so much time chasing dollars, worrying about dollars, and counting dollars. It may surprise you to learn that satisfaction with life is no more likely among the rich.

Consider this for a moment: in this country, more people buy lottery tickets than vote. We all want to be rich. At least we all think we want to be rich. But lottery winners often find that instead of enjoying a lifetime of happiness because of their wealth, they face family feuds and disputes with friends. These events take away much of what the winner really valued in the first place. Ask one Illinois man who won thirteen million dollars, then weeks later received divorce papers and a demand for half the money from his wife.

There is a new movement in the U.S. called the minimalists. These are people who have decided to live on less money. They buy less, spend less, make less, and have less stuff. They also spend less time at work and more time with their friends and family. The minimalists have made a conscious conclusion that money did not buy them what they wanted most. They don't chase after money just because most people do.

you can work toward and successfully complete. Completing any goal we set for ourselves improves our confidence and satisfaction and steadies us for the future.

Perceptions that life is meaningful, and therefore worthwhile, increase 16 percent with concrete thinking.

Lindeman and Verkasalo 1996

100

What does it all mean? You decide.

Your future—how you feel about it, yourself, and everything else—
follows from the decisions you make, the priorities you develop,
and the perspective you see things through.

☺   ☺   ☺

Great unanswered questions plague us, century after century. Why are we here? What are we supposed to be doing? What
does this all matter? Answers to these questions are so very hard
to come by because the truth lies not within someone else, but
within you. You have been given life, and with it you have been
given the opportunity to define it. Your life's path and purpose
will be drawn on a map created by you.

☺   ☺   ☺

In a study that followed the exploits of over 100 adults for a
period of two years, it was found that the effect of "good" and
"bad" events quickly faded. That is, subjects' happiness was
not dependent on the sum of events but on what they made of
those events.

Suh, Diener, and Fujita 1996

Sources

Abdel Khalek, A., O. Al-Meshaan, and A. Al-Shatti. 1995. "Themes of Presleep Thoughts." *Journal of the Social Sciences* 23: 63.

Acquino, J., D. Russell, C. Cutrona, and E. Altmaier. 1996. "Employment Status, Social Support, and Life Satisfaction." *Journal of Counseling Psychology* 43: 480.

Adams, D. 1983. "The Psychological Development of Professional Black Women's Lives and the Consequences of Career for Their Personal Happiness." Ph.D. diss., Wright Institute, Berkeley, California.

Aine, D., and D. Lester. 1995. "Exercise, Depression, and Self-Esteem." *Perceptual and Motor Skills* 81: 890.

Al-Amri, A., and M. Lee. 1996. "The Relationship Between Job Satisfaction and Life Satisfaction." *Journal of the Social Sciences* 24: 289.

Alaoui-Ismaieli, O., O. Robin, H. Rada, A. Dittmar, and E. Vernet-Maury. 1997. "Basic Emotions Evoked by Odorants." *Physiology and Behavior* 62: 713.

Argyle, M., M. Martin, and L. Lu. 1995. "Testing for Stress and Happiness: The Role of Social and Cognitive Factors." In *Stress and Emotion.* Washington, DC: Taylor and Francis.

Bailey, R., and C. Miller. 1998. "Life Satisfaction and Life Demands in College Students." *Social Behavior and Personality* 26: 51.

Barofsky, I., and A. Rowan. 1998. "Models for Measuring Quality of Life: Implications for Human-Animal Interaction Research." In *Companion Animals in Human Health.* Thousand Oaks, CA: Sage.

Bartels, K. 1991. "Humor, Fitness, Happiness, and Cardiorespiratory After Pulse as Components of Wellness." Ph.D. diss., Iowa State University, Ames, Iowa.

Battmann, W. 1996. "Resources, Stability and the Pursuit of Happiness."

In *Processes of the Molar Regulation of Behavior.* Scottsdale, AZ: Pabst Science.

Bhargava, S. 1995. "An Integration-Theoretical Analysis of Life Satisfaction." *Psychological Studies* 40: 170.

Bless, H., G. Clore, N. Schwarz, and V. Golisano. 1996. "Mood and the Use of Scripts." *Journal of Personality and Social Psychology* 71: 665.

Botwin, M., D. Buss, and T. Shackelford. 1997. "Personality and Mate Preferences." *Journal of Personality* 65: 107.

Brebner, J. 1995. "Testing for Stress and Happiness: The Role of Personality Factors." In *Stress and Emotion: Anxiety, Anger, and Curiosity.* Washington, DC: Taylor and Francis.

Brebner, J., J. Donaldson, N. Kirby, and L. Ward. 1995. "Relationships Between Happiness and Personality." *Personality and Individual Differences* 19: 251.

Brebner, J., E. Greenglass, P. Laungani, and A. O'Roark. 1996. *Stress and Emotion: Anxiety, Anger, and Curiosity.* Washington, DC: Taylor and Francis.

Brown, J., and K. Dutton. 1995. "The Thrill of Victory, the Complexity of Defeat: Self-Esteem and People's Emotional Reaction to Success and Failure." *Journal of Personality and Social Psychology* 68: 712.

Caproni, P. 1997. "Work/Life Balance: You Can't Get There from Here." *Journal of Applied Behavioral Science* 33: 46.

Cautela, J., and W. Ishaq. 1996. *Contemporary Issues in Behavior Therapy: Improving the Human Condition.* New York: Plenum.

Chand, M. 1990. "An Inquiry into the Factors of a Successful Marriage." Ph.D. diss., Jadavpur University, Calcutta, India.

Chang, E., and A. Maydeu-Olivares. 1997. "Optimism and Pessimism as Partially Independent Constructs: Relationship to Positive and Negative Affectivity and Psychological Well-Being." *Personality and Individual Differences* 23: 433.

Chebat, J., C. Gelinas-Chebat, A. Vaninski, and P. Filiatrault. 1995. "The Impact of Mood on Time Perception, Memorization, and

Acceptance of Waiting." *Genetic, Social, and General Psychology* 121: 411.

Chen, N. 1996. "Individual Differences in Answering the Four Questions for Happiness." Ph.D. diss., University of Georgia, Athens, Georgia.

Chumbler, N. 1996. "An Empirical Test of a Theory of Factors Affecting Life Satisfaction." *Journal of Psychology and Theology* 24: 220.

Clark, F., M. Carlson, R. Zemke, F. Gelya, K. Patterson, and B. L. Ennevor. 1996. "Life Domains and Adaptive Strategies of a Group of Low Income, Well Older Adults." *American Journal of Occupational Therapy* 50: 99.

Clark, A., A. Oswald, and P. Warr. 1996. "Is Job Satisfaction U-Shaped in Age?" *Journal of Occupational and Organizational Psychology* 69: 57.

Coghlan, C. 1989. "An Examination of Community Action Participation." Master's thesis, University of Texas, Arlington.

Condon, R. 1997. "Happiness and Worthwhileness." Ph.D. diss., University of California, Los Angeles.

Cramer, D. 1995. "Life and Job Satisfaction." *Journal of Psychology* 129: 261.

Crist-Houran, M. 1996. "Efficacy of Volunteerism." *Psychological Reports* 79: 736.

Daley, A., and G. Parfitt. 1996. "Good Health—Is It Worth It? Mood States, Physical Well-Being, Job Satisfaction and Absenteeism in Members and Non-members of a Health and Fitness Club." *Journal of Occupational and Organizational Psychology* 69: 121.

Diener, E., and C. Diener. 1996. "Most People Are Happy." *Psychological Science* 7: 181.

Diener, E., and M. Diener. 1995. "Cross-Cultural Correlates of Life Satisfaction and Self-Esteem." *Journal of Personality and Social Psychology* 68: 653.

Diener, E., and F. Fujita. 1995. "Resources, Personal Strivings, and Subjective Well-Being." *Journal of Personality and Social Psychology* 68: 926.

Emmons, R., and H. Kaiser. 1996. "Goal Orientation and Emotional Well-Being: Linking Goals and Affect Through the Self." In *Striving and Feeling*. Mahwah, NJ: Erlbaum.

Falkenberg, A. 1998. "Quality of Life." *Journal of Socio-Economics* 27: 1.

Fernandez-Dols, J., and M. Ruiz-Belda. 1995. "Are Smiles a Sign of Happiness?" *Journal of Personality and Social Psychology* 69: 1113.

Ferroni, P., and J. Taffe. 1997. "Women's Emotional Well-Being." *Sexual and Marital Therapy* 12: 127.

Field, D. 1997. "Looking Back, What Period of Your Life Brought You the Most Satisfaction?" *International Journal of Aging and Human Development* 45: 169.

Finch, J., M. Barrera, M. Okun, W. Bryant, G. Pool, and A. Snow-Turek. 1997. "The Factor Structure of Received Social Support: Dimensionality and the Prediction of Depression and Life Satisfaction." *Journal of Social and Clinical Psychology* 16: 323.

Fisher, B. 1995. "Successful Aging, Life Satisfaction, and Generativity in Later Life." *International Journal of Aging and Human Development* 41: 239.

Fontane, P. 1996. "Exercise, Fitness, and Feeling Well." *American Behavior Scientist* 39: 288.

Forest, K. 1996. "Gender and Pathways to Subjective Well-Being." *Social Behavior and Personality* 24: 19.

Francis, L., L. Brown, and D. Lester. 1998. "Happiness as Stable Extraversion." *Personality and Individual Differences* 24: 167.

Furnham, A., and H. Cheng. 1997. "Personality and Happiness." *Psychological Reports* 80: 761.

Garrett, R. 1996. "Wisdom as the Key to a Better World." In *Contemporary Issues in Behavior Therapy*. New York: Plenum.

Gerwood, J., M. LeBlanc, and N. Piazza. 1998. "The Purpose in Life Test and Religious Denomination." *Journal of Clinical Psychology* 54: 49.

Gilovich, T., and V. Medvec. 1995. "Some Counterfactual Determinants of Satisfaction and Regret." In *What Might Have Been*. Mahwah, NJ: Erlbaum.

Glass, J. C., and G. Jolly. 1997. "Satisfaction in Later Life." *Educational Gerontology* 23: 297.

Grove, K. 1987. "The Paradox of Happiness." Ph.D. diss., University of California, San Diego.

Hagedorn, J. 1996. "Happiness and Self-Deception: An Old Question Examined by a New Measure of Subjective Well-Being." *Social Indicators Research* 38: 139.

Hakanen, E. 1995. "Emotional Use of Music by African American Adolescents." *Howard Journal of Communications* 5: 124.

Haw, C. 1995. "The Family Life Cycle." *Psychological Medicine* 25: 727.

Heatey, K., and D. Thombs. 1997. "Fruit-Vegetable Consumption Self-Efficacy in Youth." *American Journal of Health Behavior* 21: 172.

Henry, C., and S. Lovelace. 1995. "Family Resources and Adolescent Family Life Satisfaction in Remarried Family Households." *Journal of Family Issues* 16: 765.

Hogstel, M., and L. Curry. 1995. "Ego Integrity Versus Despair in Later Years." *Journal of Clinical Geropsychology* 1: 165.

Hong, L., and R. Duff. 1997. "Relative Importance of Spouses, Children and Friends in the Life Satisfaction of Retirement Community Residents." *Journal of Clinical Geropsychology* 3: 275.

Hong, S., and E. Giannakopoulos. 1995. "Students' Perceptions of Life Satisfaction." *College Student Journal* 29: 438.

Hsieh, C. 1997. "Financial Well-Being and Happiness Among Middle Age and Old Age Americans." Ph.D. diss., University of Pennsylvania, Philadelphia, Pennsylvania.

Hunter, M., and K. L. Liao. 1995. "Problem-Solving Groups for Mid-Aged Women in General Practice." *Journal of Reproductive and Infant Psychology* 13: 147.

Jacob, M., and V. Guarnaccia. 1997. "Motivational and Behavioral Correlates of Life Satisfaction." *Psychological Reports* 80: 811.

Jeffres, L., and J. Dobos. 1995. "Separating People's Satisfaction with

Life and Public Perceptions of the Quality of Life in the Environment." *Social Indicators Research* 34: 181.

Jou, Y., and H. Fukada. 1997. "Stress and Social Support in Mental and Physical Health." *Psychological Reports* 81: 1303.

Judge, T., E. Locke, C. Durham, and A. Kluger. 1998. "Dispositional Effects on Job and Life Satisfaction." *Journal of Applied Psychology* 83: 17.

Kean, R., S. Van Zandt, and N. Miller. 1996. "Exploring Factors of Perceived Social Performance, Health and Personal Control." *International Journal of Aging and Human Development* 43: 297.

Kehn, D. 1995. "Predictors of Elderly Happiness." *Activities, Adaptation, and Aging* 19: 11.

Krug-Fite, J. 1992. "Predicting Marital Happiness from Personality Differences Between Partners." Ph.D. diss., Georgia State University, Atlanta, Georgia.

Kwan, V., and M. Bond. 1997. "Pancultural Explanations for Life Satisfaction." *Journal of Personality and Social Psychology* 73: 1038.

Lackovic-Grgin, K., and M. Dekovic. 1996. "Social Support and Self-Esteem in Unemployed University Graduates." *Adolescence* 31: 701.

Lanier, L., G. Privette, S. Vodanovich, and C. Bundrick. 1996. "Peak Experiences." *Journal of Social Behavior and Personality* 11: 781.

Lepper, H. 1996. "In Pursuit of Happiness and Satisfaction in Later Life: A Study of Competing Theories of Subjective Well-Being." Ph.D. diss., University of California, Riverside.

Li, L., D. Young, H. Wei, Y. Zhang, Y. Zheng, S. Xiao, Wang, and X. Chen. 1998. "The Relationship Between Objective Life Status and Subjective Life Satisfaction with Quality of Life." *Behavioral Medicine* 23: 149.

Lindeman, M., and M. Verkasalo. 1996. "Meaning in Life." *Journal of Social Psychology* 136: 657.

Lipkus, I., C. Dalbert, and I. Siegler. 1996. "The Importance of

Distinguishing the Belief in a Just World for Self Versus for Others." *Personality and Social Psychology Bulletin* 22: 666.

London, T. 1997. "The Case Against Self-Esteem: Alternate Philosophies Toward Self That Would Raise the Probability of Pleasurable and Productive Living." *Journal of Rational-Emotive and Cognitive Behavior Therapy* 15: 19.

Lu, L. 1996. "Coping Consistency and Emotional Outcome." *Personality and Individual Differences* 21: 583.

Lu, L., and J. Shih. 1997. "Sources of Happiness: A Qualitative Approach." *Journal of Social Psychology* 137: 181.

Lu, L., J. Shih, Y. Lin, and L. Ju. 1997. "Personal and Environmental Correlates of Happiness." *Personality and Individual Differences* 23: 453.

Lundqvist, L., and U. Dimberg. 1995. "Facial Expressions Are Contagious." *Journal of Psychophysiology* 9: 203.

Lykken, D., and A. Tellegen. 1996. "Happiness Is a Stochastic Phenomenon." *Psychological Science* 7: 186.

Lyubomirsky, S. 1994. "The Hedonistic Consequences of Social Comparison: Implications for Enduring Happiness and Transient Mood." Ph.D. diss., Stanford University, Palo Alto, California.

Lyubomirsky, S., and L. Ross. 1997. "Hedonistic Consequences of Social Comparison." *Journal of Personality and Social Psychology* 73: 1141.

Maddux, J. 1997. "Habit, Health, and Happiness." *Journal of Sport and Exercise Psychology* 19: 331.

Madigan, M. J., D. Mise, and M. Maynard. 1996. "Life Satisfaction and Level of Activity." *Activities, Adaptation, and Aging* 21: 21.

Magen, Z., M. Birenbaum, and D. Pery. 1996. "Experiencing Joy and Sorrow." *International Forum for Logotherapy* 19:45.

Mano, H. 1997. "Affect and Persuasion." *Psychology and Marketing* 14: 315.

Marshall, G., M. Burnam, P. Koegel, and G. Sullivan. 1996. "Objective Life Circumstances and Life Satisfaction." *Journal of Health and Social Behavior* 37: 44.

McGregor, I., and B. Little. 1998. "Personal Projects, Happiness, and Meaning: On Doing Well and Being Yourself." *Journal of Personality and Social Psychology* 74: 494.

McIntosh, W., T. Harlow, and L. Martin. 1995. "Linkers and Nonlinkers: Goal Beliefs as a Moderator of the Effects of Everyday Hassles on Rumination, Depression, and Physical Complaints." *Journal of Applied Social Psychology* 25: 1231.

Minetti, M. 1997. "Women's Educational Pursuits: Effects on Marital and Relationship Happiness." Master's thesis, University of Nevada, Las Vegas.

Monteiro, I. 1991. "Enrichment, Nurture, and Resource." Ph.D. diss., Catholic University of America, Washington, D.C.

Mookherjee, H. 1997. "Perception of Well-Being Among Older Persons in Nonmetropolitan America." *Perceptual and Motor Skills* 85: 943.

Murray, C., and M. J. Peacock. 1996. "A Model-Free Approach to the Study of Subjective Well-Being." In *Mental Health in Black America.* Thousand Oaks, CA: Sage.

Myers, D., and E. Diener. 1995. "Who Is Happy?" *Psychological Science* 6: 10.

Neto, F. 1995. "Predictors of Satisfaction with Life." *Social Indicators Research* 35: 93.

Ng, Y. 1996. "Happiness Surveys." *Social Indicators Research* 38: 1.

Niedenthal, P., and J. Halberstadt. 1997. "Being Happy and Seeing Happy." *Cognition and Emotion* 11: 403.

Noor, N. 1996. "Some Demographic, Personality, and Role Variables as Correlates of Women's Well-Being." *Sex Roles* 34: 603.

Notarius, C. 1996. "Marriage: Will I Be Happy or Will I Be Sad?" In *A Lifetime of Relationships.* Pacific Grove, CA: Brooks/Cole.

Oates, W. 1997. "Reconciling with Unfulfilled Dreams at the End of Life." In *The Aging Family.* New York: Brunner/Mazel.

O'Connor, B. 1995. "Family and Friend Relationships Among Older and Younger Adults." *International Journal of Aging and Human Development* 40: 9.

Oropesa, R. 1995. "Consumer Possessions, Consumer Passions, and Subjective Well-Being." *Sociological Forum* 10: 215.

Otta, E., and F. Abrosio. 1996. "Reading a Smiling Face." *Perceptual and Motor Skills* 82: 1111.

Panos, K. 1997. "Linking: An Exploration of Related Constructs and Effects on Happiness." Master's thesis, American University, Washington, D.C.

Parducci, A. 1995. *Happiness, Pleasure, and Judgment: The Contextual Theory and Its Applications*. Mahwah, NJ: Erlbaum.

Parker, D. 1996. "The Relationship Between Time Spent by Older Adults in Leisure Activities and Life Satisfaction." *Physical and Occupational Therapy in Geriatrics* 14: 61.

Parr, V. 1997. "How to Feel Good Without Feeling Good About Yourself." *Journal of Rational-Emotive and Cognitive Behavior Therapy* 15: 5.

Pavot, W., F. Fujita, and E. Diener. 1997. "The Relation Between Self-Aspect Congruence, Personality, and Subjective Well-Being." *Personality and Individual Differences* 22: 183.

Pegalis, L. 1994. "Frequency and Duration of Positive Affect: the Dispositionality of Happiness." Ph.D. diss., University of Georgia, Athens, Georgia.

Pettijohn, T. 1996. "Perceived Happiness of College Students Measured by Maslow's Hierarchy of Needs." *Psychological Reports* 79: 759.

Pilcher, J. 1998. "Affective and Daily Event Predictors of Life Satisfaction in College Students." *Social Indicators Research* 43: 291.

Pilcher, J., and E. Ott. 1998. "The Relationship Between Sleep and Measures of Health and Well-Being in College Students: A Repeated Measures Approach." *Behavioral Medicine* 23: 170.

Rahman, T., and A. Khaleque. 1996. "The Purpose in Life and Academic Behavior Problem Students." *Social Indicators Research* 39: 59.

Ramanaiah, N., and F. Detwiler. 1997. "Life Satisfaction and the Five-Factor Model of Personality." *Psychological Reports* 80: 1208.

Ramanaiah, N., F. Detwiler, and A. Byravan. 1995. "Sex-Role

Orientation and Satisfaction with Life." *Psychological Reports* 71: 1260.

Rogers, S. 1996. "Mothers' Work Hours and Marital Quality." *Journal of Marriage and the Family* 58: 606.

Ruch, W., G. Koehler, and C. Van Thriel. 1997. "To Be in Good or Bad Humor." *Personality and Individual Differences* 22: 477.

Scherpenzeel, A., and W. Saris. 1996. "Causal Direction in a Model of Life Satisfaction." *Social Indicators Research* 38: 161.

Schyns, P. 1998. "Crossnational Differences in Happiness." *Social Indicators Research* 43:3.

Scope, E. 1999. "A Meta-Analysis of Research on Creativity." Ph.D. diss., Fordham University, New York, NY.

Scott, V. B., and W. D. McIntosh. 1999. "The Development of a Trait Measure of Ruminative Thought." *Personality & Individual Differences* 26: 1045.

Seybolt, D., and M. Wagner. 1997. "Self-Reinforcement, Gender-Role, and Sex of Participant in Prediction of Life Satisfaction." *Psychological Reports* 81: 519.

Shank, M., and F. Beasley. 1998. "Fan or Fanatic: Refining a Measure of Sports Involvement." *Journal of Sport Behavior* 21: 435.

Sheehan, E. 1995. "Affective Responses to Employee Turnover." *Journal of Social Psychology* 135: 63.

Sherer, M. 1996. "The Impact of Using Personal Computers on the Lives of Nursing Home Residents." *Physical and Occupational Therapy in Geriatrics* 14: 13.

Simpson, R. 1990. "Conflict Styles and Social Network Relations as Predictors of Marital Happiness." Ph.D. diss., University of Michigan, Ann Arbor, Michigan.

Sirgy, M. J., D. Cole, R. Kosenko, and H. L. Meadow. 1995. "A Life Satisfaction Measure." *Social Indicators Research* 34: 237.

Smail, D. 1995. "Power and the Origins of Unhappiness." *Journal of Community and Applied Social Psychology* 5: 347.

Smith, R. 1997. "Experiencing Negative Affect." Master's thesis, American University, Washington, DC.

Solomon, J. 1996. "Humor and Aging Well." *American Behavior Scientist* 39: 249.

Staats, S., M. Armstrong-Stassen, and C. Partillo. 1995. "Student Well-Being: Are They Better Off Now?" *Social Indicators Research* 34: 93.

Sugarman, S. 1997. "Happiness and Population Density." Master's thesis, California State University, Long Beach, California.

Suh, E., E. Diener, and F. Fujita. 1996. "Events and Subjective Well-Being: Only Recent Events Matter." *Journal of Personality and Social Psychology* 70: 1091.

Takahashi, K., J. Tamura, and M. Tokoro. 1997. "Patterns of Social Relationships and Psychological Well-Being Among the Elderly." *International Journal of Behavioral Development* 21: 417.

Taylor, C. 1988. "Assessment of Happiness Among Young Adults." Ph.D. diss., Iowa State University, Ames, Iowa.

Tepperman, L., and J. Curtis. 1995. "A Life Satisfaction Scale for Use with National Adult Samples from the USA, Canada, and Mexico." *Social Indicators Research* 35: 255.

Thakar, G., and G. Misra. 1995. "Correlates of Daily Hassles Among Dual Career Women." *Journal of the Academy of Applied Psychology* 21: 93.

Thurman, C. 1981. "Personality Correlates of the Type A Behavior Pattern." Ph.D. diss., University of Georgia, Athens, Georgia.

Tom, G., T. Schmidt, and M. Deuber. 1995. "The Materialistic Orientation of Business Students." *College Student Journal* 29: 106.

Turner, C. 1994. "Follow Through in Conflict Resolution as a Factor in Marital Satisfaction and Personal Happiness." Master's thesis, University of Nevada, Las Vegas, Nevada.

Van Dijk, W., and J. Van Der Pligt. 1997. "The Impact of Probability and Magnitude of Outcome on Disappointment and Elation." *Organizational Behavior and Human Decision Processes* 69: 277.

Van Overwalle, F., I. Mervielde, and J. De Schuyter. 1995. "Structural Modeling of the Relationships Between Attributional Dimensions,

Emotions, and Performance of College Freshmen." *Cognition and Emotion* 9: 59.

Veenhoven, R. 1996. "Developments in Satisfaction Research." *Social Indicators Research* 37: 1.

Voydanoff, P., and B. Donnelly. 1998. "Parents' Risk and Protective Factors as Prediction of Parental Well-Being and Behavior." *Journal of Marriage and the Family* 60: 344.

Warburton, D. 1995. "Effects of Caffeine on Cognition and Mood Without Caffeine Abstinence." *Psychopharmacology* 119: 66.

West, C., D. Reed, and G. Gildengorin. 1998. "Can Money Buy Happiness?" *Journal of the American Geriatrics Society* 46: 49.

Williams, A., D. Haber, G. Weaver, and J. Freeman. 1998. "Altruistic Activity." *Activities, Adaptation, and Aging* 22: 31.

Wilson, S., C. Henry, and G. Peterson. 1997. "Life Satisfaction Among Low-Income Rural Youth in Appalachia." *Journal of Adolescence* 20: 443.

Wrzesniewski, A., C. McCauley, P. Rozin, and B. Schwartz. 1997. "Jobs, Careers, and Callings: People's Relations to Their Work." *Journal of Research in Personality* 31: 21.

Wu, P. 1998. "Goal Structures of Materialists vs. Non-Materialists." Ph.D. diss., University of Michigan, Ann Arbor, Michigan.

Contents

Introduction

Jennifer Peterson is a doctor who, not surprisingly, highly values her occupation. She's seen the best it can do and has been moved by the lives she has touched through her job. But she also has a nagging frustration over the people she worries neither she nor any other physician will be able to help.

Her concern is based not on the limits of medical science but on the limits of communication. "In a national survey, fewer than one in five men said they would seek medical care if they were sick or in pain," Dr. Peterson said with alarm. "At the same time, nine out of ten said their doctor was excellent. Imagine that for a moment. There is nearly unanimous agreement that their doctor was excellent—and that their doctor was to be avoided if at all possible." At the same time, Dr. Peterson says, surveys of doctors reveal widespread concern that too many patients live in fear of medical treatment and fail to realize the many steps they can take to improve their health both in the short term and over the course of their lives.

Dr. Peterson is all too familiar with studies that describe people who have suffered with conditions for years. One day a traffic accident or some unforeseen circumstance brings them into emergency contact with a physician. The patients, almost against their will, find themselves receiving treatment they could have had years earlier for their preexisting condition. Often, their delay has tragic repercussions.

If there is one thing Dr. Peterson would like to say, not only to her patients but to everyone, it is that you should no more fear or ignore your health than you would fear or ignore any other basic need. "Ignoring your health, whether it means your daily habits or a medical condition you have, does not make any sense and will not help you today, tomorrow, or down the road. When you are hungry you eat, but before you are hungry you plan how to get food. It should be the same with your health. When you are sick you see a doctor, but before you are sick you should plan on how to be well."

Dr. Peterson sees a clear role for both medicine and medical information in people's lives. "Doctors can help you when you are sick, and of course you should visit us then. But health information can help you throughout the rest of your life. You can make a change. You can do things sensibly, approach things rationally, use a strategy, and create the best outcome possible for yourself."

No book can take the place of a doctor, of course. "Consult a doctor about your condition or about important health changes in your life or about your looming fears. But read up on medical research to help you in your daily activities. You can avoid common practices that harm us and embrace common practices that sustain us." A book about health issues, Dr. Peterson says, "just needs to give people basic information they can use, because many will. And people will be healthier. Lives will be lengthened and strengthened."

Dr. Peterson's concerns and advice guided me as I conducted the research for this book, combing through studies on habits, practices, and attitudes that affect our health. Each entry in *Simple Secrets of Healthy People* presents the conclusions of doctors and scientists. Each entry presents the core scientific finding, an example of the principle, and the basic advice health professionals recommend. It is intended as a tool for you to help examine your habits and attitudes with an eye toward being able to be a positive force for health in your own life.

Acknowledgments

My thanks to Gideon Weil, Liz Winer, and the staff of HarperSanFrancisco, and to Sandy Choron, my agent.

1

Use a Plan, Not a Piecemeal Approach

When a house is built, all the steps of the process have to be considered before construction starts. Otherwise, you could wind up installing the doors and then finding out the refrigerator won't fit through them. Similarly, your health plans have to be considered together as a whole instead of one piece at a time. Your chances of sticking to a health improvement plan—eating right, exercising regularly, or quitting smoking—are higher if you focus on your overall health rather than just the task at hand. In other words, think about the things that you could do to improve your health and how they fit together, and each act will reinforce everything else you are trying to do.

Six years ago, Lee was hobbling around with a cane. Now the seventy-two-year-old Chicago area man pumps iron for more than two hours a day several times a week. "I call it a lifestyle change," he says.

"There was a time when I wasn't in very good shape. I was about fifty pounds too heavy, had swelling in my knees, and was loaded with arthritis," he says. But he got tired of living like what he calls an "old man."

"I did research on nutrition, read studies and books on preventing aging," Lee says. He started changing his diet and exercising. "I have seen so many improvements. I sleep better, have more energy, stopped having stomach problems, and my aches and pains went away."

Lee adds, "I feel like I'm forty."

Now Lee is taking his enthusiasm for healthy living on the road. He speaks about nutrition and exercise to various community groups and is putting together his health tips on a Web site.

One of his biggest fans is Kristina, who is forty years younger than Lee. "I heard him give a presentation, and I was so impressed with Lee. He asked me if I was ready to change my life and I said I was," Kristina said. She has since changed her habits and feels better than ever. "If anyone would have told me a seventy-two-year-old retiree would change my life, I wouldn't have believed it," she said, "but now I know better."

Dana-Farber's Center for Community-Based Research studied workplaces where employers provided health, safety, and quitting smoking programs as one comprehensive service, and workplaces where such programs were offered separately. At the end of two years, the investigators found that more than twice as many workers quit smoking and maintained a healthy diet in the comprehensive service as in the separate programs.

2

The Quest for a Perfect Body Is Doomed

Seeking a healthier lifestyle is an inherently good thing that will help you in many ways in your life. But seeking a perfect outcome—the perfect body—is neither good nor helpful. When we seek a perfect outcome, we set ourselves up for failure. In reality perfection does not exist because for every improvement we make, we can always think of something else that could be changed. Seek a healthy body that functions, not a perfect body fit for a display case.

Comedian and former talk show host Rosie O'Donnell has battled a weight problem for as long as she can remember. Rosie decided to start a club to encourage the overweight to improve their habits and fitness. Seeking a fitness coach, she said, "I didn't want some Barbie doll type saying, 'You can do it, you can do it.' Anyone who sees that is going to think, 'I'm never going to look like that, why bother?' People would give up before they started."

For the club's head fitness coach, Rosie hired Judy Molnar, who stands six feet one inch and weighs two hundred pounds. "When I first met Judy," Rosie said, "I thought, 'Here's someone who looks like me, looks like a regular person.'" Judy's message—"If I can get fit, anyone can"—resonated with Rosie.

A few years before, Judy had begun walking for her health. At the time, she weighed three hundred pounds. "For the first time in my life," she recalled, "it wasn't about a diet. It wasn't about getting to a certain body size. It was about my health." Gradually her walking routine became a running routine. And while she was not focused on losing weight, it began to happen, "one doughnut at a time." After a year she had lost a hundred pounds.

When O'Donnell's club sponsored a run, she had a chance to meet countless club members. "These people told me I inspired them," Rosie said. "Well, they inspired me."

According to a study by the U.S Department of Health and Human Services, more than 98 percent of people surveyed named something they wanted to change about their bodies, with their weight being the most frequently mentioned feature.

3

Avoid Imagining the Worst

When something is wrong with us, we can easily imagine the worst outcome. We know the doctor is going to tell us how horrible our situation is and how awful the recommended treatment is. This process of exaggerating the threat not only creates anxiety; it also has the dangerous effect of encouraging us not to seek treatment. Don't let yourself get caught in a guessing game that does you no good. Acknowledge what you don't know, and find out the best answer from a medical professional.

🐚 🐚 🐚

Why do so many people with medical needs avoid going to see a doctor? "That's the biggest question for all of us," says Dr. Ed Hayer of South Carolina.

"'The doctor says' is an awfully weighty phrase," according to Dr. Hayer. "For a lot of people, there's a feeling that the news the doctor brings will never be good, the answers will be hard or painful, and that knowing their fate would be a terrible burden."

In Dr. Hayer's field, cardiac medicine, this feeling can be disastrous. "We can do so much more the earlier we see a patient with heart problems. And fear is one of the major obstacles to seeing patients when we need to. What can happen is that fear of a terrible diagnosis actually helps create the terrible diagnosis because if the patient had not been fearful and had come in sooner, their outcome would be better."

Dr. Hayer finds that communicating with people who have already been treated for cardiac trouble is much easier. "People fear the unknown, and in some respects, they have an easier time dealing with the recovery process once they've seen the medical process up close."

Dr. Hayer's advice for those who are worried about seeking medical care is to understand the value of information. "No one will force a treatment on you. You are free to walk away, to seek a second opinion. We're here to help you." Once you make the commitment to seek medical treatment, "Know that you'll always be in charge. Write down questions you want answered. Speak up if you feel rushed or confused. Ask about alternative treatments. Get a second opinion. But get the information you need. It could save your life."

In a study of those who suffer back pain, University of Michigan researchers found that people were ten times more likely to think surgery was necessary than was actually the case.

4

Keep Healthy Foods Handy

People will eat what's available to them. You will be amazed at how much less junk food you consume when you make it difficult to get. If you don't regularly buy junk food, how often are you going to want a chip so badly that you would be willing to walk to the store and buy a bag? By the same token, if you make healthy foods easily available, your likelihood of choosing a piece of fruit for a snack rises dramatically. Be strategic about your food choices when you are not hungry, and you will be much more health oriented when you are.

Gloria knows about the importance of eating habits. As a physician, she advises patients about how much and what foods they should eat. As a person, she struggles to eat right and maintain a healthy weight.

"I come from a long line of really big women. I was destined to be big," she says. And while she rejects drastic diets, she knows and lives with the importance of eating right for her health.

Gloria's house is full of fruit, available anytime for her four children. Junk food snacks are absent. And they eat a home-cooked meal every night to reduce the temptations of large portions and unhealthy foods they would find in a restaurant.

"Would I prefer it if I had lived my life at, like, 125 pounds? Well, yeah, definitely," she says. "But we have to start swapping the way we see things. We have to get away from the blame game and all the shame, all the worry, and get focused on health. And the way to do that is to surround yourself with what you should have and keep what you shouldn't have out of reach."

University of North Carolina researchers found that for every additional supermarket in their neighborhood, people become 32 percent more likely to eat their recommended daily portion of fruits and vegetables—just because affordable and nutritious foods were more readily available.

5

Easy Does It with Vitamins

If vitamins are helpful, then more vitamins must be even better for us, right? It doesn't work quite that way. In some cases, the recommended dosage of a vitamin is all our body can process. In others, taking more than the recommended dosage is harmful. You should make sure your body gets the necessary vitamins and minerals humans need but resist the urge to devise your own supervitamin strategy.

"Taking too much of an essential vitamin or mineral may be as dangerous as going without the nutrient at all," says Dr. Beverly McCabe-Sellers, professor of dietetics and nutrition at the University of Arkansas Medical Sciences School. She notes the importance of the latest warning from the Institute of Medicine, the nonprofit arm of the National Academy of Sciences that for decades has created guidelines on how much of each essential nutrient a person needs. "In the most recent of a series of reports updating nutrients' value to the human body, the institute sets upper limits—the maximum amount an individual may take without risks of adverse health effects—for such things as vitamin A, copper, iron, manganese, and zinc," Dr. McCabe-Sellers notes.

Dr. McCabe-Sellers thinks the report needs to be understood by consumers because she has seen far too many cases of people "megadosing" on vitamin supplements by taking five or even ten times the recommended dietary allotment for a nutrient.

"Although men require 900 micrograms of vitamin A each day and women 700 micrograms, some supplements offer as much as 7,500 micrograms in a single dose. That's more than twice the level set by the National Academy of Science report as a dangerous overdose."

Adds Dr. McCabe-Sellers, "This is definitely a situation where you can get too much of a good thing."

Doctors at Dana-Farber's Cancer Institute in Boston have found that people exceeding the recommended daily allowance of vitamins and minerals can worsen the effects of cancer and reduce the effectiveness of conventional cancer therapies.

6

What You Do Matters

Health is not like the lottery. We are not just randomly stricken with diseases. While some health outcomes are completely beyond our control, many diseases are affected by our decisions and behaviors.

Karen has seen more than her share of sickness in her family. Both her parents died of cancer, and she agonized as they suffered through its last stages.

She read everything she could on the subject to try to help her parents. "I tried to help, but there were no miracles available. But what I did learn is that anyone can drastically reduce their chances of suffering from major diseases like cancer. And I felt I owed it to my parents to try to live a healthy life in their memory."

Karen embraced eating right and exercising as major facets of her life. "It not only makes you healthier; it just makes you feel better," she said. "That's the bottom line."

Karen took up running, hiking, and resistance training. Karen's interest in the subject even led to a midlife career change. She became an exercise physiologist, a person who teaches approaches to exercising.

Karen's work now includes not only teaching exercising to help prevent disease but also introducing exercise programs to those suffering from cancer, because research show exercise improves a patient's prospects for recovery.

Today, she can't imagine living her life any other way. "If I sit at home, then I'm going to feel awful."

Cancer is the number one public health fear. Most people believe it is impossible or next to impossible to prevent cancer. Researchers at the Mayo Clinic found, however, that half of all cancers can be traced to personal choices such as having a sedentary lifestyle, a high-fat diet, prolonged and unprotected exposure to the sun, and use of tobacco.

7

Give Yourself Time

The average person feels that there isn't enough time in the day. We rush around from one thing to the next, not stopping until the day is over. One of the easiest things to cut out of the day is a moment for ourselves. But time spent quietly alone is not a luxury. It is an important component of how we function. Give yourself time to sit, to think, to feel—every single day.

Told to shut his eyes and shake his body vigorously with his limbs gyrating like rubber bands, Kevin began to reconsider whether he should have signed up for this.

"Is this guy for real?" wondered the New York City firefighter as he began Dr. Jim Gordon's program of meditation, yoga, and alternative healing therapies to help firefighters deal with the emotional stress of the September 11 attacks.

The workshop took place not long after the end of the nine-month cleanup of human remains and World Trade Center debris. Now, Kevin meditates and "shakes" stress away nearly every day.

"It really calms you down," said Kevin, who is helping Dr. Gordon launch a regular program for city firefighters.

Dr. Gordon, picked by President Clinton to head a two-year White House Commission on Complementary and Alternative Medicine Policy, has used similar workshops to help survivors of war in Kosovo and Bosnia. The founder of the Center for Mind-Body Medicine in Washington, he decided to adapt the program for firefighters.

But how do you get a firefighter to stretch out on a mat in a yoga pose, meditate to soft music, or learn to breathe steadily—practices Dr. Gordon says most first-timers think are "ridiculous and crazy"?

"What we say is, 'Look, you're practical people; try it for yourself and see if it makes a difference,'" Dr. Gordon said. "The bottom line for them is, 'Okay, Doc, I never heard of this stuff before, but if it can help, let's check it out.'"

Kevin wants to recruit more of his colleagues to Dr. Gordon's program by explaining that it is a take-charge, independent type of therapy that should appeal to tough-minded firefighters. "It's just basic things that you can do to help yourself."

Researchers at the University of Wisconsin found that people who meditated regularly had higher levels of disease-fighting antibodies.

8

Stop the War on Bacteria

We have antibacterial soap, antibacterial cleaners, even antibacterial cooking surfaces. Unfortunately, the war against bacteria has two important—and harmful—side effects. First, by limiting our exposure to bacteria, we prevent ourselves from building up our immune system, our internal defenses. This can make the effects of a bacterial-based illness in the future that much more serious. Second, by constantly attacking bacteria with our various products, we are killing the vast majority of bacteria but also contributing to the survival of the fittest, whereby the remaining bacteria become resistant to our measures and wind up stronger than they would have been if we hadn't tried to kill them. While you should obviously wash your hands and be very careful with uncooked foods, there is no reason to douse yourself or your home with antibacterial cleaners at every opportunity.

Cleanliness is next to godliness, we are taught, but is it possible to become so clean that it's not good for us? That's the question posed by Stuart Levy, a Tufts University geneticist.

All that scrubbing and sponging with new antibacterial soaps and detergents may be weakening our immune systems, Dr.

Levy says. It is killing helpful germs and spurring the growth of mutant strains of super bacteria, he contends.

Dr. Levy longs for the long-ago days when children built strong immune systems, in part, by getting dirty. He wants us to use the cleaners our parents trusted: plain soap and water. Dr. Levy says he has seen no evidence to show that antibacterials work to benefit health.

"Our modern obsession with protecting ourselves from every germ, every dog hair, and every fleck of dust might be backfiring. That arsenal of cleaning products in our cupboards might be our undoing. It seems that our immune systems have been so coddled by antibacterial soap and Lysol that they don't build up the musculature to fight off disease," Dr. Levy laments.

"We are fast becoming a society with an immune system so fragile that even the unpleasantness and misfortunes of daily life send us reeling. We know now, more than ever, that insulating ourselves from pain and fear isn't possible," Dr. Levy warns.

Hackensack University Medical Center doctors found that much of the bacteria on the skin is protective. It is there to prevent harmful bacteria from flourishing and making you ill. If that bacteria is not there, it cannot do its job. Scrubbing with antibacterial soap removes the good bacteria along with the bad.

9

You're Never Too Old to Improve Your Habits

"It's too late to improve my health." Many people think their habits are set, and even if they could change them, what good would it do? In fact, improving your habits can improve your health at any age. There's no value to lamenting what you didn't do for yourself in the past, but there is tremendous value in thinking about what you can do for yourself in the future.

Richard doesn't call himself a senior citizen. And those who have seen him compete in triathlons probably wouldn't call him that either.

At sixty-six years of age, he has won his age division in eight triathlons, sometimes finishing ahead of men half his age. The triathlons include a four-hundred-meter swim followed immediately by a twenty-kilometer bicycle ride followed immediately by a five-kilometer run.

One of the trickiest parts to a triathlon, according to Richard, is the transitions, especially when you have to get out of the water and get your bike equipment on. Because the clock never stops, "You just have to try to go as fast as you can," he says.

"My last triathlon had about two hundred competitors. It was fun to be one of the fastest ones. This one was open to anyone over fifty. There were a man and a woman between seventy-five and eighty years old who did the triathlon. There was also an eighty-six-year-old woman who did it as a relay with her sixty-two-year-old son," Richard said.

Richard has no plans to slow down or give up triathlons. "I believe age is just a number, and life is what you make it."

Case Western Reserve University researchers found that increasing the frequency of exercise among those over the age of seventy-two improved their overall health and was associated with a better outlook on life and a 20 percent longer life span.

10

Don't Buy the Fountain of Youth

The claims are tempting. Look younger! Feel younger! Reverse the effects of aging! And do all that in a pill or a cream. These are claims with no basis in reality, however. You cannot buy youth. In fact, you not only will waste your money, but you might do yourself harm in the process. Instead, focus your energy on habits and behaviors that reduce the effects of aging.

The simple fact is, "No currently marketed intervention has yet been proved to slow, stop, or reverse human aging," says Dr. Jay Olshansky of the University of Illinois at Chicago.

Dr. Olshansky regularly warns consumers about anti-aging products that he says make outrageous claims. One such product touts its use by Princess Caroline of Monaco, John Wayne, Yul Brynner, Anthony Quinn, Natalie Wood, Red Buttons, Fred MacMurray, and many other worldwide dignitaries, including members of the KGB before Communism fell. As Dr. Olshansky notes, "Ironically, not only is the inventor of the product dead; so are many of the people he brags about having used his product."

He adds, "This is just one of many products being sold throughout the world with the claim that it will slow or reverse human aging. These products have never been proven to do anything but line the pockets of those selling them."

Dr. Olshansky warns, "Although there is reason to be optimistic that scientists will eventually be able to intervene in one or more processes associated with human aging, it is not currently possible to buy a product that will stop or reverse aging."

Americans spend more than $15 billion every year on anti-aging products. According to a report by the U.S. General Accounting Office, none have been subject to government testing, and a majority are considered potentially harmful by government doctors.

Always Being Right Is Wrong for Your Health

People with a very high estimation of themselves and little respect for others wind up experiencing more stress and anger as they deal with a world that constantly disappoints them. Thinking yourself always right is neither a helpful social trait nor a sound health habit. See the value in other people's perspectives, even if you highly value your own.

"Feeling that you are better than everybody else, or feeling that you are always right, might seem empowering. But really it's mostly isolating. It leads to a tremendous amount of tension," says Dr. James Coyne, a professor of psychiatry at the University of Pennsylvania.

The medical implications are great. "We've seen everything from tooth decay to ulcers to heart problems linked to this very basic ability to get along."

In addition to preventing medical problems, the ability to feel connected to others aids the recovery process. "Even when your own determination to get better wavers, the connections to others put you back on track," Dr. Coyne says.

Ultimately, bullheadedness can turn into a matter of life and death. Dr. Coyne and his colleagues videotaped heart patients' arguments in their homes and grouped them according to the negativity of their interactions. Those heart patients who were more negative toward the other person in arguments were 1.8 times as likely to die within four years as those who were given less negative ratings. "That's powerful stuff," Dr. Coyne said.

Researchers at the University of Bradford in England found that 62 percent of absolutist thinkers—people with a very high opinion of themselves and a low tolerance for compromise—suffered from high levels of anger and stress, which depressed the functioning of their immune systems.

12

Couch Time Affects Body and Mind

Rest is a crucial part of our lives—but only in moderation. Too much time on the couch or the recliner degrades the ability of our bodies and minds to function. Just as you wouldn't expect a car to function well if you left it in the garage for twenty years and then tried to drive it, you can't expect your body and mind to be vigorous if you don't use them regularly.

Mary raked in the winnings as the top scorer among the bridge players at the Beachwood Community Center in northeast Ohio. "I made a killing," she said, smiling, as she scooped $6.50 in coins into her handbag. But that's not why she plays. "It keeps your mind going." Her fellow players agree.

They may not know it, but new research may prove they're on to something. Playing bridge, or any kind of social and intellectual activity, really does keep the mind going—and with it, the body.

Neurologist Robert Friedland of Case Western Reserve University School of Medicine says, "There is a growing number of studies supporting the theory that an active mind keeps the brain and body healthy. The brain is like any other organ in the body," he says. "It ages better, with more health and better function, when it is used."

Seen under a microscope, the brain tissue of an Alzheimer's patient is clogged with plaque deposits, consisting of abnormally clumped proteins, he explains. There is also a loss of connections between brain cells, which become tangled. But mental activity increases the flow of blood to the brain, increases the connections of nerve cells to each other, and increases the resistance to disease. The healthy brain is better fortified to battle the debilitating effects of the plaque and tangles should they occur.

The thinking brain is like a star athlete—through regular practice it can simply outperform. And any kind of activity that uses the brain can fortify it. Learn a musical instrument, take a Shakespeare class, study Portuguese, Dr. Friedland says. And for Mary and her friends, that means keeping the cards coming.

For seven years researchers at Columbia University in New York tracked almost two thousand people aged sixty-five and older. Those who engaged in leisure activities that required active brain use—reading, playing a game, even just talking with friends—reduced their risk of Alzheimer's by 38 percent. Conversely, the more time people spent inactive—lounging on the couch—the slower their brain response was to stimuli and the weaker their immune system became, making them more susceptible to debilitating disease.

13

Eat Your Spinach

Foods rich in folate, a form of vitamin B, help reduce the risk of stroke and heart disease. Eating two servings a day of foods like tomatoes, leafy green vegetables such as spinach and romaine lettuce, pinto, navy, or kidney beans, and grain products decreases levels of an amino acid that contributes to the process underlying heart disease and stroke.

Despite its high nutrient content, and Popeye's best efforts, most people don't ask for spinach every day. But researchers at the University of Arkansas have found a simple solution—put spinach on your sandwiches instead of iceberg lettuce. Even better, they found you can't taste the difference.

Marjorie Fitch-Hilgenberg, a professor of nutrition, has been working on the project intended to slip a little more nutrition into food. "We know that people don't eat the recommended number of servings of vegetables, and as a result, they're missing out on the nutrients these vegetables provide," Professor Fitch-Hilgenberg said. "With spinach, we realized we could make a small change to the food people already eat and have a significant impact on their nutritional status."

When they tested their idea, by secretly replacing iceberg lettuce with spinach on a variety of sandwiches, tasters rated the sandwiches with spinach equally as tasty as the ones with lettuce. Also, none of the tasters suspected the switch. "Only one or two people mentioned that the lettuce looked very green," Professor Fitch-Hilgenberg said. "That's as close as they got to guessing."

In addition to testing her theory at work, Professor Fitch-Hilgenberg said she's already made the switch at home, recently giving her daughter and husband tacos with spinach instead of lettuce. "A lot of spinach disappeared," she said. "I've had no complaints. I put it in salads all the time. If you don't tell them, they won't notice."

Researchers at Tulane University found that people who consumed at least two servings of folate-rich foods per day had a 20 percent lower risk of stroke and a 13 percent lower risk of cardiovascular disease. Unfortunately, only 32 percent of all American adults are getting enough folate every day.

14

You Can Worry Your Health Away

Feeling out of control, feeling a sense of dread, and feeling inadequate are not only threats to your disposition; they are threats to your health in general. When we feel more vulnerable, we are less likely to maintain healthy habits. We turn to unhealthy and excessive behaviors to comfort ourselves, but the relief is quite temporary, while the health effects are lasting.

"Stress helps account for two-thirds of family doctor visits and, according to the U.S. Centers for Disease Control and Prevention, half the deaths to Americans under sixty-five. It has been implicated in heart, stomach, and mental disorders, along with the more ordinary headaches, backaches, and high blood pressure and cholesterol. My study of medical students found decreased levels of the body's natural killer cells, which fight infections and tumors, during stressful times such as exam periods," says Dr. Janice Kiecolt-Glaser of Ohio State University.

Hormones produced during the stress response include adrenaline and cortisol. While they are energy boosters, they are also potent inhibitors of our immune system, Dr. Kiecolt-Glaser says. "This constant activation of the fight-or-flight response causes various systems of the body to develop chronic problems, such as high blood pressure or a strained heart."

Dr. Kiecolt-Glaser does not advise people to think in terms of eliminating stress, which is probably impossible. Instead, people need to take steps to ensure that they do not destroy themselves with the stresses and anxieties in their lives.

Among Dr. Kiecolt-Glaser's medical students, the ones who diligently practiced relaxation techniques during exam weeks "showed significantly better immune function during exams" than those who did not.

Researchers at the University of California, Irvine, found that people who experienced high levels of anxiety were up to seven times more likely to practice poor health habits.

15

Fitness Is Free

The impressive-looking exercise machines we see advertised on television make it seem like we better save up if we're going to start exercising. In reality, the foundation of any good exercise program need be no more complicated than taking a walk or jog for free. Expensive machinery and health club memberships are fine if you want them but are not required for you to improve your health.

* * *

Linda has been strolling the paved paths of Oglebay Park in Wheeling, West Virginia, for twenty years, but she has more company these days.

A barrage of television and newspaper ads promoting the health benefits of walking has helped get thousands off the couch and onto trails throughout the city. The ads resulted in a 32 percent increase in the number of people who walk for at least thirty minutes, five days a week.

While Americans spent nearly $6 billion on home-exercise equipment last year, Linda doesn't see the need. "Walking is the nicest exercise you can do," Linda says after a brisk morning outing with her dog. "You don't have to get all kinds of equipment. You can do it with a friend. You can do it alone. You can do it as fast or as slow as you want."

Walking makes Linda feel better physically and psychologically, boosting her energy level when she is tired. "I like being outside," she adds. "And I like getting exercise without having to kill myself."

ॐ ॐ ॐ

University of Richmond studies found that fitness programs based on walking or jogging and exercises without equipment, such as sit-ups, have the same beneficial health effects as machine-based exercise regimens.

16

The Cold Doesn't Give You a Cold

"Button up or you'll catch cold." Age-old advice we've all heard from parents and grandparents. The truth is, though, that temperature does not cause colds. Colds are caused by viruses transmitted person to person. The best way to keep from getting a cold is to wash your hands so you prevent the spread of the virus through contact.

The sickness we call a cold is called a cold in most languages of the world. The idea that being cold can give you a cold has been widely held for centuries. Yet science has found no evidence for it.

One of the first studies on the matter more than a half century ago took a group of volunteers and exposed half to warm temperatures and half to cold. There was no difference in their likelihood of catching a cold. Indeed, we know today that colds are common at every latitude and longitude in the world from the deserts to the Arctic.

Some of the most interesting studies on the subject have come from small, isolated communities such as island villages. Among these is a 1931 field study of Longyear City, an Arctic coal mining settlement on the island of Spitsbergen, midway between the Norwegian mainland and the North Pole. For seven months of the year, the town's five hundred residents were iced in, and during that time colds were almost nonexistent. However, the arrival in port of the first ship of summer invariably brought with it a full-blown cold epidemic—leading researchers to conclude that being cold, by itself, is irrelevant to catching a cold.

University of Texas researchers found that more than half of the people surveyed thought they could catch a cold by not wearing a coat in winter or by going outside with wet hair. Almost 60 percent believed chilly weather could cause a cold. Less than 10 percent correctly responded that a virus is required to transmit a cold from person to person.

17

Healthy Living Is an Attitude

What is the difference between someone who has healthy habits and someone who doesn't? It's not ability. Anyone can choose to eat better foods or avoid unhealthy habits. It's not inclination. Everyone prefers being healthy to the alternative. It is, however, attitude. Specifically, an optimistic view of one's own ability to engage in healthy habits is the most important ingredient in actually following those healthy habits.

Sue hit the wall in the spring of 2001.

At age forty Sue, a mother of three, had tried dieting for years. She was used to zippers not zipping and buttons not buttoning. But the straw that broke the camel's back, motivating her to drop seventy pounds? Not finding a dress at the mall.

"I couldn't find anything that fit me in the stores," says Sue, who made up her mind that day to lose weight.

"Losing the weight is just the beginning. Keeping it off is the hard part. It's a lifestyle change. You have to watch what you eat, and you have to exercise. You'll find you feel better when you do. You can't go back to your old habits."

Sue adds, "You have to set reasonable goals. That's what I did. I said, 'I want to have so much off by summer. I want to have so much off before I go visit my parents, enough so they can see a difference.' Then I said, 'I want to have so much off by Christmas,' and Christmas is when I met my goal."

Sue thinks that most people are overwhelmed before they even start. "They think it will be too hard, that they are not strong enough to make a change. But I found that you can do this in small steps—small steps toward leading a balanced life."

She explains, "No one can do this for you. It's more true of health habits than just about anything in life. But if you have the right attitude about your family, your work, and your health, you can see that everything in your life is interconnected and that the reason you can succeed in health is the same reason you can succeed in anything you care about doing."

Doctors at Cornell University conducted a study of recently pregnant women and found that the single best predictor of their eating and exercise habits after pregnancy was not their physical condition or their weight, but their belief in their own ability to take care of themselves.

18

Cleaning Isn't Clean

While the point of cleaning your house is to make it cleaner, the process of cleaning your house actually makes things worse. Cleaning stirs up dust, hair, dander, and other powerful allergens. Ironically, those who schedule their big cleaning of the year to coincide with the arrival of spring are leaving themselves doubly vulnerable because they will increase the spread of allergens inside their house just when the amount of allergens outside their house is peaking. Be prepared for a health drain that accompanies cleaning, and avoid taking on too big a cleaning task at one time.

"I don't know anybody who enjoys vacuuming," Carla says. "It's not fun to begin with, then it stirs up so much in the air that I can't stop sneezing."

The solution for Carla was a robot.

"Robots are not just for the Jetsons anymore," Carla says. Robots can vacuum your house or mow your lawn, among other sneeze-inducing tasks. "It's good for people who are short on time, elderly people, lazy people, people with handicaps, and allergy sufferers."

The robot scans the size of the room and then can automatically cover the space without any human input. "It may not look like the robots in the movies," she says of the machine that looks like a large radio on wheels, "but this one is real, and it saves time, trouble, and my nose." Carla happily adds, "I let it do its work, then I enjoy the clean floor."

For most people, allergies interfere with many aspects of quality of life, including getting a good night's sleep (68 percent), doing outdoor activities (53 percent), being able to concentrate (50 percent), and being productive at work (43 percent). The American Academy of Allergy, Asthma, and Immunology reports that allergies are the sixth leading cause of chronic disease in the United States, and four out of five people with allergies experience heightened symptoms when cleaning the house.

19

History Isn't Everything

It is often true that having a certain disease in your family history increases the risk of your getting the disease. But that does not mean you are likely to get the disease or that you are powerless to improve your chances of avoiding the disease. Knowing your family history should help you be better informed about potential risks, but it should not be a source of alarm.

For Kate, it started with a health assignment her son received in school. "He was supposed to create a family tree, with health information included. Four generations of mental and physical ailments."

Kate soon found out how difficult it can be to assemble that information. "I had most of the information for my parents, my aunt and uncle, but I had trouble with my grandparents, and my great-grandparents were people I had never met. My husband's side of the family is big, with a lot of brothers and sisters in each generation, and is spread out across the country."

Spurred on originally by an interest in helping her son with the assignment, Kate became engrossed in the investigation. "It was like police work, tracking people down, putting the information together. I really became fascinated with the information and its implications for my husband, my son, and me."

There were roadblocks. Some distant family members did not want to answer the questions. Some family members' histories were hard to reconstruct over time.

Several weeks later, though, her son had finished the family tree. It lists predisposition, disease frequency, and the potential for everything from hypertension to depression. It is a document Kate is storing in a safe place for her son's children, and their children, so that this health history will not be lost.

Kate understands both the power and limits of this information. "Too many people discover their family medical history only after disaster has struck in the form of cancer, heart attack, alcoholism, or other heartbreaking diseases. But this is not a call to panic. It is a call to prepare and empower. We have to remove fear from this process and to understand our vulnerability."

❧ ❧ ❧

The Mayo Clinic reports that only 5 percent of cancer diagnoses have hereditary origins.

20

Don't Delay—Emergencies Can't Wait

When an emergency strikes, will you immediately call for help? While the answer would seem obvious, most people fail to act quickly, and even when they decide to act, they fail to call for help. When emergency situations occur, we must throw out our normal habits of caution and restraint and immediately seek the help of professionals.

The sink in the bathroom was running, and firefighters found a container of water nearby after they dragged the man, unconscious, from an intensely hot and smoky apartment fire in Syracuse, New York.

As stunned neighbors watched, firefighters laid the man on a snowy driveway, pumped his chest, and puffed oxygen into his lungs. They could not save him.

It appears he tried to douse the flames himself before smoke overwhelmed him, authorities said. He did not dial 9-1-1. "People think they can tolerate the smoke conditions because they watch movies like *Backdraft,* which is ridiculous," said Syracuse fire lieutenant Jeff Sargent.

The fire was so hot that the couches were scorched to their springs and the television melted to its tube.

"The only message is, 'Get out,'" said John Cowin, Syracuse fire chief. "A small fire doubles every minute. This is an unfortunate situation. Whenever you are dealing with a fire emergency, a police emergency, or a medical emergency, call it in immediately. Give us a chance to do our jobs."

Doctors at the University of Alabama at Birmingham found that nearly half of almost 800,000 heart attack patients they studied drove themselves or were driven by a friend or family member to the hospital instead of calling 9-1-1 for an ambulance. This occurred even though emergency medical personnel can cut in half the time it takes to receive potentially lifesaving treatments such as clot-buster drugs.

21

Enjoy Slow Music at Dinner

Our eating habits often have little to do with the biological need for food. We get into certain food routines for all kinds of reasons, such as convenience and comfort. Use your habits to reduce your tendency to overeat without depriving yourself of the food you need. Here's one powerful strategy: Listen to slow music while eating, and your meal will take longer to eat and result in your eating less.

Michael suffered from weight and health problems throughout his childhood. Now he runs a fitness camp for children in New England.

He knows that kids feel like they are being sent off to prison when they arrive. "Most of the children are scared to death. They think this is going to be bread and water and lockdowns."

Instead, Michael emphasizes the need for realistic changes, including smaller portions, better nutrition, and more activity. "The campers are so busy with skating, climbing, and paddle boats that they seldom think about food during the day. They realize they are having fun here and that they are safe here because no one will make fun of them."

To keep the intensity just right, Michael also relies on music. "Music sets the tempo for what we are doing. During activity times, we turn up the fast-paced music the children like to hear. During dinnertime, we have something slower that I like to hear. We tend to mimic the pace of music we listen to, so the fast music encourages activity while the slow music helps to encourage a more patient approach to eating."

Researchers at Johns Hopkins University found that music affects how fast we eat: the average diner eats five mouthfuls a minute when listening to lively music, four mouthfuls a minute when listening to no music, and three mouthfuls a minute when listening to a slow melody.

22

Avoid Tanning Beds

Too much exposure to the sun is dangerous and is a leading precursor to skin cancer. Natural sunlight is far less dangerous than tanning beds.

Gayle was, by her own admission, a sun worshiper for most of her life. Summer found her on the beach, and during the off-season she visited tanning beds up to five times a week.

"I was dark. I was very, very dark," says Gayle. "I look back at it now and say, 'How vain.'" The radical change in Gayle's perspective took place after she had a checkup and heard some distressing news.

Sitting on an examination table, dressed in a paper gown and awaiting her doctor, Gayle casually asked the nurse what she thought about a mole high on Gayle's right leg. The nurse strongly suggested she show it to her doctor, who in turn sent Gayle to see a dermatologist. Immediately.

Three days later, Gayle was sitting at her desk at work, receiving the test results from the previous day's biopsy. "The doctor called me and told me it was malignant and how far it had gone," Gayle remembers. "I thought I was ready for the news, but I wasn't."

Gayle had Stage III melanoma, signifying a relatively thick melanoma that had spread to the lymph nodes. Gayle had started down a path that would lead to a pair of surgeries, the removal of fifteen lymph nodes from the right side of her body, and an anguished stretch of time during which she was not sure she would survive.

Gayle, already preparing for the worst, was left trying to cope with her new reality. "I cried a lot," she says. "I was in total denial. I thought there was no way it could happen to me. I found it hard to believe because I thought I was healthy. I looked healthy. I had a tough time believing I could be so sick and feel so healthy."

Fortunately, her disease was caught in time, and doctors have now given her a clean bill of health. "It was just so silly," Gayle says about her days spent in tanning booths. "One thing the cancer has done for me is help me realize the rest of my life will not be devoted to silliness."

Doctors at the Mount Sinai School of Medicine in New York City found that tanning beds expose the body to ten to fifteen times higher concentrations of dangerous ultraviolet rays than does natural sunlight.

23

A Tomato a Day Is Even Better

While most fruits and vegetables have a lot more food value when eaten raw, the tomato retains its health effects even after it's cooked. Including tomatoes or tomato sauce in your diet at least five times a week significantly reduces the risk of many major diseases.

"An apple a day keeps the doctor away, the old saying goes. But it's probably time to acknowledge a tomato a day is even better," says Dr. Roger Mason. "New research is continually expanding our understanding of the positive health effects of tomatoes."

Dr. Mason says that lycopene, an organic component that turns the tomato red, is the key ingredient that helps reduce incidence of certain cancers and heart disease. "Lycopene is an antioxidant, a substance that protects the body from cell and tissue damage."

Dr. Mason explains, "Better yet, it's not just a raw tomato that scores high on the health charts. Processed tomato sauces, used in pizza and on spaghetti, may be even better at warding off some diseases than the tomato slices in your salad. This means that the tomato in the forms people already like to eat the most is a tremendous health tool."

In fact, cooked tomatoes contain up to 2.5 times as much lycopene. "Everybody thinks if you process food, you lower the nutritional value. But as it turns out, that is not true for tomatoes," Dr. Mason said.

Five servings of tomatoes a week in any form—canned, raw, cooked, in soups, sauce, ketchup, or juice—provides enough lycopene to cut the risk of cancer and heart disease in half and to improve the health of lungs, eyes, and the skin, report scientists at Ohio State University.

24

It's Easier to Practice Good Health When Those Around You Do Too

While we are all capable of making decisions on our own, we often let ourselves be influenced by people around us. If we see our family, friends, and neighbors out taking long walks or jogging, we are more likely to participate. In contrast, if people around us have unhealthy habits, we are more likely to ignore the importance of health. Pay attention to the good examples around you, and if you don't have any, understand you will have to set the good example.

They used to be a family that sat around together. Now they are a family that exercises together.

Chris and Theresa, forty-something parents of ten-year-old Danny, decided that the family should get out and exercise more. They had very different motivations—Chris was concerned about his overall fitness, Theresa wanted to improve chronic back problems, and Danny felt confined by a school day without recess or gym class. However, they realized they would all do more if they did it together.

They now go to the gym together at least once a week. Chris favors the elliptical trainer, Theresa likes the weight machines, and Danny does a bit of everything.

"We exercise together all the time," Theresa said. "Alone, I couldn't get motivated to do it. It's easier to back out when no one else is involved. But now it's a family project, it's a team, and the motivation is always there."

According to a University of Minnesota study, people who described their friends and neighbors as having favorable attitudes toward exercise and healthy eating were 19 percent more likely to have healthy exercise and eating habits themselves.

25

Physical Health Is Mental Too

The best enjoyment of life follows the pursuit of the care and feeding of both your body and your mind. Symptoms of distress in your life need to be understood in the context of your entire body, not just the immediate area affected. Think of health as a broad goal for both your body and your mind.

In the golf world, it is known as the yips. The muscles of the hands and wrists spontaneously contract, making it nearly impossible to putt. What was supposed to be an easy three-foot putt can end up feeling like a fifteen-foot putt when a golfer loses control because of the yips. The famous golfer Ben Hogan was afflicted with the yips, and the condition ended his career in professional golf. Experts believe the yips can add five strokes to an affected golfer's eighteen-hole score.

"For many years the yips was seen as a purely psychological problem, something that was all in the golfer's head," says Dr. Aynsley Smith of the Mayo Clinic Sports Medicine Center. "We've found that there is both a physical component and mental component to most yippers.

"We studied highly accomplished golfers who experience the problem after many years of successful competition, and we see similar fine motor problems in others, such as professional musicians, who must assume unnatural postures for prolonged periods. On the other hand, in some others, anxiety appears to the underlying problem," says Dr. Smith.

The Mayo Clinic researchers are staging a putting tournament of their own with yippers, including some whose symptoms seem primarily physical and some whose symptoms seem primarily mental. By measuring factors such as confidence, heart rate, grip force, and stress hormones and by studying the videotapes of each putt, they hope to better understand the problem and offer the best physical and mental treatments to relieve the symptoms.

Doctors at Duke University found that patients with a physical ailment who received a combination of physical and mental therapies were 2.5 times more likely to maintain recovery long-term than patients who received treatment for only their physical condition.

26

Breathe Right

Proper breathing is probably the easiest and most powerful way to protect your health. It results in better digestion and circulation, more restful sleep, decreased anxiety, and a more stable heart rate.

Faced with massive road snarls during her daily commute, Julia, who lives in Atlanta, started reading up on breathing. She was surprised at the idea that something all of us do all the time could be improved so dramatically with a little thought and effort. Now, breathing right is her way of relieving stress while stuck in traffic.

"We all carry chronic tension in our lives," Julia says. "We don't even realize how much there is." Traffic jams can aggravate that tension and turn normally easygoing people into irritable road warriors, she adds.

"I know that when I'm coming down the road and I see traffic is backed up, that stress response automatically kicks in," she says. "Your heart rate speeds up, the muscles in your neck and arms begin to contract. Every muscle in your body is preparing for fight or flight. The problem is, you're not going to fight or flee. You're stuck in traffic, and unless you do something right away, that stress response will stay in your body for hours or even days."

Julia's method is the one experts favor. "Take deep breaths. Let your abdomen rise like a balloon as you inhale, filling it all the way. As you exhale, let your abdomen gently relax back toward your spine."

🐚 🐚 🐚

Researchers at Harvard University found that breathing slowly and deeply from the abdomen triggers a blood flow boost to the brain and up to a 65 percent reduction in stress.

27

Use Discretion with Internet Advice

When we go car shopping, we have our defenses ready. We know how to separate out the fluff and be wary when we're told about the perfect condition of the car and its kindly former owner who rarely drove it. But when it comes to the Internet, we are often vulnerable to foolhardy claims. We need to bring our skepticism with us even when we desperately want easy answers to important health concerns.

"Patients with cancer and other life-threatening conditions often turn to complementary or alternative medicine for a variety of reasons, and a major source of their information is the Internet," says Dr. Scott Matthews of the University of California, San Diego. However, he cautions, "there is a staggering amount of medical misinformation on the Internet."

Matthews and his colleagues reviewed 194 Internet sites with information on alternative medicine treatments. In their review of the Internet sites, the researchers looked at whether the treatments were for sale online, whether the sites provided "patient testimonials," if the treatment was touted as a "cancer cure," and if the treatment claimed to have "no side effects."

A yes answer to any of the questions raised a red flag for the researchers, suggesting that the Internet site's scientific accuracy was exaggerated or questionable. The researchers found that up to 90 percent of sites raised at least one red flag.

"When patients search the Internet for information on a topic for which there is little objective clinical research, use of these red-flag questions may help identify questionable sites," Dr. Matthews notes. "Internet sites with one or more red flags should be avoided. However, no red flags for any particular site does not ensure scientific accuracy."

Patients who've read of Dr. Matthews's study have thanked him, he says, for "helping them weed out some of the danger and the make-believe in health information."

A Tufts University study found that more than 60 percent of Internet users visit Web sites for health advice, and more than 90 percent believe that advice is reliable.

28

Mold Is Everywhere—So Relax

There are one hundred thousand different kinds of mold. You can find many of them in just about any home. The vast majority of those mold types are harmless, however. Despite the sometimes scary headlines, small amounts of mold in your home don't mean you will wind up with a serious illness and don't mean you have anything to fear.

Steve makes his living from mold. His Arkansas company cleans heating and cooling duct systems to remove mold. And business has been booming.

"Every time there's a story on the news about mold in homes, we get ten calls."

Steve says he finds mold in every home he visits, but he also admits, "Is it that black deadly mold? I couldn't tell you.

"As long as we have humidity, moisture, and leaks," Steve adds, "we're going to have mold problems. Mold is here to stay."

As for advice, Steve says that households need to think about reducing the likelihood of major mold problems. Repair water leaks promptly, vent bathrooms, and reduce indoor humidity with vents, dehumidifiers, or air conditioners. And though it wouldn't be good for business, Steve admits, "People shouldn't be panicking about this."

The Mayo Clinic reports that most people have no adverse reaction to mold. Scientists have been unable to substantiate reports of mold-induced chronic ailments.

29

Turn Off the TV

Television is a passive activity for our bodies and our brains. Unlike just about anything else we might do with our time, viewing television requires almost no thought or action. It has the same effect on our brain that sitting on the couch has for our body. Turn off the television, especially when there isn't something you specifically want to watch, and go do something, anything, else. It will make you healthier.

Floundering while she waits for her job prospects to improve, Jody spends at least ten hours every day watching television. The shows are generally the same: talk shows until noon, then news, then as many versions of *Law & Order* reruns as she can find. Most weekends, channel surfing is all the exercise Jody gets.

Jody knows her fascination with television is in many ways dangerous. She knows she can't allow the TV to become her only window on the outside world. But by the time she dies, Jody estimates, she will have spent at least a quarter of her life sitting in front of the tube.

Her situation is becoming increasingly frustrating to her. "I just want other people to know: Don't just sit around on the sofa thinking one day everything is going to be okay. That's how I let my life slip by, and now I regret it."

Jody flips through some old photos of herself, contemplating all the time she has spent wasting away in her bedroom watching TV. "I will never get any of that time back," she says. "I could have done so much. I really would have liked to have had more of a life."

Excessive television viewing in middle age triples the danger of developing brain diseases such as Alzheimer's later in life, according to doctors at the Case Western Reserve University School of Medicine.

30

Drive Safely—When It's Safe

When driving, your safety depends not just on you but on the other drivers. The vast majority of the more than 46,000 deaths due to car accidents in the United States every year are from multicar crashes, not single-car accidents. Avoid the mentality that you can and should drive any time you want to. Avoid driving at times that attract reckless drivers.

Rob teaches a defensive driving course outside of Pittsburgh. He emphasizes not just the skills of driving but also the decisions of driving.

One is the choice of speed. Your speed matters, of course, but your speed relative to the other cars is crucial. "A big gap—in either direction—between your speed and the prevailing speed on a road is a recipe for disaster. It is the differences in the speed of vehicles on the highway, particularly major highways like interstates, that create the most problems. Equally problematic are the dawdlers who cause brake lights behind to crescendo in red and the hot-shoes who try to slalom through traffic ten or fifteen miles an hour faster than anybody else. Go with the flow, or get off the highway."

A second decision is the route. "Know the dangerous intersections, the curves that people take too fast, the streets without adequate lighting. There's no reason to put yourself in a dangerous spot when you know the roads."

And the third decision is timing. "Don't go out there whenever you want to. We know that there are more drunk drivers on the road later on weekend nights. And if you want to be a safe driver, you will factor in that you can't be a safe driver unless the other cars on the road are driven by safe drivers."

There is a 41 percent increase in driving fatalities throughout the United States on the night of the Super Bowl. This exceeds the surge in accidents on any other occasion, including New Year's Eve, report researchers at the University of Toronto.

31

Eat Less, but Eat Often

When you are trying to cut back on the amount of food you eat, you'll be tempted to cut back on the number of times you are eating. After all, if you are trying to reduce calories, isn't it easiest to reduce the number of meals? This strategy, however, is a recipe for failure. Aside from the difficulties you might experience because of hunger from skipping meals, eating fewer times per day reduces the efficiency of our bodies in processing food as fuel. In other words, skipping meals maximizes the caloric effect of the food we do eat.

Michelle has won and lost battles with her weight at least four times during the past decade, dropping as much as sixty pounds—and then gaining much of it back after meeting her goal and losing the excitement of the challenge.

She's tried expensive meal plans and visited a personal nutritionist in the past. But when she decided once again to confront her expanding waistline, she opted for the Internet. She already belonged to an online book club, and the idea of turning to the computer for information, support, and inspiration seemed like a natural.

"I considered going to meetings in person, but I tend to not have a lot of time," said Michelle, who found what she was looking for in a free online community.

"There are just tons of groups and sites out there," Michelle said. "For whatever kind of thing you want to do, I'm sure there's a group in existence already for it."

She now logs in twice a day to read the few dozen messages that are posted, and she participates in the weekly weigh-in. After ten weeks she's lost seven pounds—a result she's happy with.

"I like to see other people dealing with similar issues and getting ideas from other people in the group," Michelle said.

Michelle has led a group discussion on the subject of skipping meals. "There is no way to make that work. Going to the gas station less often does not make your car use less gas; it just means you run out of gas and shut down the whole system. Eating fewer times does not make your body eat less; it just means you are even more hungry when you do eat, you eat more, and your system is less well prepared to handle it."

A study at Oxford University found that people who ate five or six times a day had a 5 percent lower total cholesterol and were 45 percent more likely to be able to sustain their target weight than people who ate once or twice a day.

32

Look on the Bright Side

In almost everything that happens, you have the opportunity to consider the worst or the best implications. Even terrible setbacks hold within them rays of hope you might focus on. And even wonderful events can produce threads of worry or despair you might cling to. Your focus is not merely a personality quirk but a way of life. Learning to see the upside, the optimistic outcome, the good in what has happened, will not only increase your enjoyment of life; it will lengthen your life.

She's eighty-two years old. She's outlived two husbands. But Annie enjoys every day.

"I can do anything I want today," Annie says, and she just might.

"You can close yourself off, say 'poor me.' But what kind of life is that? You have to go out and see the beauty in things. There's a reason why when we're children our mothers were always sending us outside to play. Because that's where we thrive—out there doing something."

Annie says she has a daily routine that helps her focus on what's good in her life. "I wake up every morning, stand in front of a mirror, and say, 'You are gorgeous.'"

Annie has long believed that a positive mind-set goes hand in hand with good health. "You have to put your mind to it. If you are going to wait around moping, you will find out things aren't really as great as they should be, and you'll tear yourself up in the process."

ぴ ぴ ぴ

Optimistic people, who credit themselves when things go well and view bad times as temporary, live longer than pessimists. According to a study conducted over a thirty-year span by the Mayo Clinic, pessimistic people are 19 percent less likely to reach a normal life expectancy.

33

Drink Grape Juice

Much as the Teflon coating keeps food from sticking to the pan, the bioflavonoid in grape juice prevents cholesterol from sticking to our arteries. Regular consumption of grape juice therefore reduces the likelihood of clogged arteries and lowers the risk for conditions such as heart disease and strokes.

"Bioflavonoids, or compounds that act as antioxidants, fight damaging free radicals. They occur naturally in a number of foods, such as fruits and vegetables, especially apples and onions; tea, especially green tea; chocolate; nuts; and grape juice and red wine," says Dr. Michael Lefevre of Pennington Biomedical Research Center.

"The data suggests that bioflavonoids offer a protective effect against LDL, or the bad cholesterol, and improve endothelial function to keep the blood vessels dilated," he says.

Dr. Lefevre says it would be a good idea for people to look at their diets and determine whether they are consuming foods that contain bioflavonoids. "Foods are not created equal. Even foods we think of as healthy are not created equal. I try to eat a lot of green, leafy vegetables, onions, and apples. And drink things like grape juice. Grape juice is the kind of beverage that children tend to consume a lot of, and then people forget about it as they become adults. It's time to rediscover it and put a glass of grape juice in your diet every day."

In studies of people with heart disease, drinking grape juice for two weeks helped widen arteries and reduced cholesterol oxidation by more than one-third, according to doctors at Stanford University.

34

Home Affects Your Health More than Work

We know that work can cause stress and strain on us. Conventional wisdom has it that work can be the main hurdle to living a healthy life. For most people, however, your home life is a far more significant factor in your overall health than your work life. The positive effects of a good home life are greater than the negative effects of a bad work life.

Brian and Clare are in a unique position to compare the stress of home life to the stress of work life. For the first ten years after Brian graduated from law school, he was on the fast track. He worked six days a week and never even thought of taking a vacation. He found his match in Clare, an attorney whose office was down the hall and who matched him hour for hour in dedication to her job.

"I was worried about the health effects for myself in working twenty-five hundred hours a year. Of not giving myself time to compress. But I also saw it as something that would not last forever."

In their few spare hours a week away from work, Brian and Clare began dating. Two years later they were married.

When Clare got pregnant, Brian started having thoughts about dedicating himself to his family and home life full-time. "When we talked about it, Clare was clear that she didn't feel like she was finished with what she was doing. She wanted to cut back on her work but not cut out."

Brian said he "changed a lot of diapers and learned more lullabies than he ever imagined existed."

Even though their days are completely different, their nights and weekends are entirely the same. And their commitment to each other and the baby is complete. And how has the arrangement affected their health? "We both recently had checkups, and we both came through with flying colors."

Over a three-year period, researchers at the University of Toronto studied the effects of work and marriage on health. They found the strain of a person's job was unrelated to his or her blood pressure over time. People with strong marriages, though, showed an 8 percent improvement in blood pressure, while the condition of those with struggling marriages deteriorated by 6 percent over time.

35

Ask Whether a Medicine Is Right for You

The effectiveness of all kinds of medical treatments is assessed on the basis of averages. That is, a "good" treatment is one that has been effective for the average person in the past. Your particular situation may not fit that average, however. Whether choosing an over-the-counter medicine or receiving a prescription from your doctor, ask whether this medicine is meant for someone in your precise situation.

"Despite mounting evidence showing that men and women respond differently to the same drug, most physicians and their patients are still not aware that sex matters when prescribing medications. In this case, we know there's a difference, and too many in the health care field pretend that there's not," says Sherry Marts, scientific director of the Society for Women's Health Research.

Why the lack of awareness? One of the reasons is that the Food and Drug Administration and the pharmaceutical industry, groups responsible for drug labeling, only recently began to analyze safety data by gender. In fact, reporting of gender-based data analysis in medical journals, while increasing, is still not routine practice, according to Dr. Marts. This shortcoming of the system keeps gender-specific risks as well as benefits buried beneath heaps of data.

So what can you do to protect yourself from potentially harmful drugs? Dr. Marts says, "We all must demand that physicians and pharmacists fully inform us about the pharmaceuticals prescribed and their applicability to our precise condition."

According to a study conducted by Stanford University, 40 percent of medicines tested had significantly different effects on women than on men.

36

Memories Are Not Lost

Forgetting is frustrating and vexing. Why do we forget something just when we want to remember it most? Why do we forget something and then remember it hours or days later, after we have stopped trying to remember? Our memories are still lodged in our brain; they are not lost. However, we sometimes have trouble gaining access to those memories. Our brain is organized to store information in small pieces. Remembering someone's name when we meet her or him on the street requires us to retrieve first our visual memory of the person and then, separately, our memory of the name. The process can be interrupted by, among other things, our anxiety to remember. Trust yourself—the information is in there and it will come out. You just sometimes have to wait.

George is great with names. He remembers them by breaking down new information into familiar images. An ardent sports enthusiast, he remembers that Gutzon Borglum designed Mount Rushmore, for example, by thinking of tennis champ Bjorn Borg and major league baseball player Mike Lum.

"Whenever I think of Mount Rushmore, in my mind I automatically see Borg with his scraggly little beard and Mike Lum," he says.

For Sally, it often helps to associate the name with a physical feature or a trigger word. If it rhymes, all the better. Barry with the thick, wavy hair can be remembered as Hairy Barry. Or slender Jim could be Slim Jim. If rhyming doesn't work, choose a noun that is similar enough to the name that it will act as a cue. A mental image of a stove will remind you of Steve. Barbed wire will remind you of Barbara. "Creating a picture in your mind gives you some kind of concrete association," Sally says.

Dr. Harold Wolf explains that an inability to remember something is just like coming upon a road closure and having to look for alternative routes. "If a stored memory is blocked for some reason, the brain will look for different connections in order to retrieve that information. Memory techniques are simply mental detours to get to where you want to go."

By measuring the electrical rhythms that different parts of the brain use to communicate with each other, researchers at Johns Hopkins University have demonstrated that our memory of a single object requires our brain to retrieve multiple bits of information. Therefore, the inability to remember something does not mean we've forgotten it; it means there is an obstacle between the different pieces of information.

37

Ask Where Your Water Comes From

We all want to buy products that are healthy for us. And water is the healthiest drink. It contains no calories and is necessary for our bodies to function. Bottled water is selling at a record pace as more than half of all Americans are trying to drink more. The importance of water, unfortunately, has led to great hype and endless sales pitches. Water from the tap and pricey bottled water from a store have the same health benefits, and sometimes they're exactly the same thing.

When tested by an independent group, one-third of the most popular bottled water in California supermarkets failed to meet state water quality standards, and all of the samples—100 percent—failed to meet advertised claims of purity. The Environmental Law Foundation analyzed the water and issued a report stating, "Despite state regulations meant to ensure that all vended water meets stringent health standards, buying water is like playing a slot machine: You can't be sure what will come out."

Bill Walker, a co-author of the report, says, "It's very clear from our findings that the inflated prices that consumers in

California pay for water is a rip-off. You can't just go around making claims for your product you can't meet. They should either improve their process, or they should have to stop making that marketing claim."

Bill says the problem is that consumers are paying money to get better water than the tap water, "and they are not getting it." He adds, "If you are buying water, research it. Find out where it comes from and what they do to it before it gets to you. Otherwise, you are paying for nothing."

Researchers at the Natural Resources Defense Council discovered that 40 percent of the bottled water sold in the United States is tap water.

38

You Don't Have to Put Up with Secondhand Smoke

Whether it is for a family member or friend, or to be able to visit a favorite restaurant, many people would rather accept the burden of secondhand smoke than the costs of avoiding it. However, secondhand smoke is a serious and optional health risk. Think of it this way—you wouldn't accept a slap in the head just because other people felt like doing it.

Minnesotans have witnessed a unique statewide advertising campaign about the dangers of secondhand smoke. The ads, which appear on television, the radio, billboards, and in newspapers and buses, were produced as part of a $5.5 million anti-smoking campaign funded by Minnesota's 1998 settlement with the tobacco companies.

"Secondhand smoke kills more Americans each year than murder, drugs, and AIDS combined," said Dr. Richard Hurt, a Mayo Clinic tobacco researcher and chair of the Minnesota Partnership for Action Against Tobacco, which launched the ad campaign.

"Breathing secondhand smoke is not just a nuisance," said Dr. Hurt. He notes that children exposed to secondhand smoke are more likely to have asthma, bronchitis, and pneumonia and to die of SIDS, sudden infant death syndrome. "Hundreds of thousands of children suffer needlessly because others smoke around them."

However, most Minnesotans "don't understand how serious a problem it is," he said. The ad blitz was designed to change that.

One thirty-second TV spot shows a dead bird in a cage with a cigarette burning underneath and the message: "Secondhand smoke contains 200 poisons and 43 cancer-causing agents."

All the ads end with the same tag line: "Secondhand smoke. Still want to breathe it?"

❧ ❧ ❧

Children's exposure to secondhand smoke was found to be directly related to their mothers' attitudes. The children of those who considered secondhand smoke unhealthy were 72 percent less likely to show exposure, according to a study by Columbus Ohio Children's Hospital.

39

Forgiveness Helps You Heal

Being able to forgive, to let go of angry thoughts and feelings, promotes the body's natural ability to return from an aroused state to a normal state. Staying at an even keel allows our bodies to function at their best. For the sake of your own health, avoid holding grudges.

Drew remembers the feeling in the pit of his stomach every time he thought of it. A co-worker, someone he considered a close friend, had taken credit for his idea and was reaping the benefits of it at work.

"I could really work myself up every time I saw her, every time I thought about it. Just about anywhere and anytime I might start getting angry again."

Drew noticed, however, that his anger had little effect on his co-worker but a big effect on him. "I would be steaming, and she would be sitting there, pretending nothing was wrong. Of course, for her, nothing was wrong."

A doctor's visit confirmed Drew's suspicion that his anger was having significant effects. "My blood pressure was up, and when the doctor asked if I was under any unusual stress, I only had one explanation."

Drew decided that he could not continue to harbor anger or disappointment. While he considered the friendship irreparably harmed, he could not dwell on the past or the hurt he had felt. "I started looking to the future and realized that the only way past this situation, and the only way to reducing this stress in my life, was to let it go. It's over, I learned from it, and now it's on to a better day."

Doctors at the University of Washington found that holding a grudge raises the heart rate, blood pressure, and sweat production in more than nine out of ten people. Each of these symptoms indicates an activated nervous system and increased stress hormones.

40

Use the Stairs

Improving your health may seem to require a complicated plan and an obsessive dedication to the goal. In fact, improving your health can be as simple as changing a few habits. For one, take the stairs every day instead of the escalator or elevator. Tiny acts like that in the course of a day can have a huge effect when performed over the long term.

Nearly six in ten people experience no daily exercise.

"In many places, we've lost the ability to walk somewhere," laments Professor Harold Burton, who teaches exercise science at the State University of New York at Buffalo. "Because there are no sidewalks, or you would have to cross eight lanes of traffic, walking can be impossible. Meanwhile, with remote controls and computers, we can have just about anything we want without even getting out of our chair."

Physical activity is so rare that he suggests doing any sort of extra movement throughout the day. "Insignificant as it may sound, when shopping, park at the far end of the lot instead of cruising around for the closest space. Get rid of the remote control so that changing the channel means getting off the couch.

Take a few flights of stairs instead of making the whole trip in the elevator."

Professor Burton adds, "If you have no physical activity, anything at all that you do will help you a lot. Is it as good as working out for thirty minutes, three days a week? No. But it's much better than no exertion at all."

🐦 🐦 🐦

Researchers at the Centers for Disease Control in Washington, D.C., have found that spending ten minutes on the stairs each day could result in losing ten pounds of weight over the course of a year. The CDC encourages employers to make stairways more attractive and interesting by adding artwork to the stairways, which they found can increase stair usage by 14 percent.

41

You'll Get the Same Care on the Weekend

Many folks imagine that if they are feeling ill on the weekend they should tough it out until Monday, when the real doctors will be at work and ready to help them. While the size of a medical staff on duty at any time varies with the typical workload of the time period, the quality of medical care does not depend on the day and time treatment begins.

"I've had patients say to me that the pain started in the middle of the night, but they didn't think about getting help until the next morning," Dr. Terry Brown says. "I wish they would understand this isn't like waiting until Monday to call the plumber so you don't have to pay overtime rates. We're here all the time, and the sooner you call us, the sooner we can help."

Dr. Brown explains, "People really need to separate out emergency services from their view of everything else. Police, the fire department, hospitals—we are built for a twenty-four-hour day, every day. In an emergency, there is never a reason to wait for a better time to call us."

He adds, "We don't save the good staff for the daytime and punish the bad staff with night shifts."

While he doesn't recommend anyone show up at 2 A.M. just to verify the hospital is ready for all comers, Dr. Brown does encourage people to become informed about the health care facilities in their area. "You really should know when you can visit your doctor's office, when you can visit clinics for non-emergency treatment, and you must understand that the time you can receive help for an emergency is any time one happens."

University of Iowa doctors tracked the outcomes of over 150,000 patients in critical condition based on the day of the week they arrived in the hospital. They found patients' recovery rate did not vary based on whether they were admitted during the weekend or during weekdays.

42

Talk to Your Pharmacist

Pharmacists are often an overlooked resource on our health care team. Pharmacists can help us understand the effects of different medications we're taking, help us follow the directions in taking them, and guide us to over-the-counter products that are safe to take in light of our particular condition. Speak to your pharmacist regularly, and you will dramatically reduce the chances of making a mistake with your medications.

Larry's medications came with a dizzying array of instructions. Take with water. Take with food. Take as needed. Take until empty. Don't drive or operate heavy machinery after taking.

Each medication, Larry knew, was important. But what each did, why, and whether there was a better way, Larry had no idea.

The statistics for using medication incorrectly are grim, according to many studies on the topic. Each year in the United States, one out of six hospital admissions, one out of four nursing home admissions, one-quarter of all malpractice lawsuits, one-half of all medication failures, and 2.5 million medical emergencies can be attributed to incorrect medication use.

In one year, prescription drug–related errors cost more than $200 billion in the United States. Successful medication education could cut this by 80 percent.

"A vital part of medication education is communication between health care practitioners and patients," said Professor Jerry Cable of Ohio State University. "People always have questions. They want reassurance and accurate information from somebody they can trust."

Professor Cable's pharmacist outreach program helped answer these concerns. "We were looking for outdated medications, duplicates, and drugs that could potentially interact with other drugs. And we wanted to help people with the things they don't normally think of as drugs, such as herbs, vitamins, and creams," Professor Cable said.

For Larry, they found two drugs that were meant to address the same problem. Larry was grateful for the information.

"People need someone to have oversight over their medications, because it is too important to ignore and too complicated for most people to fully understand," Professor Cable said.

A study by researchers at Ohio State University found that people who took the opportunity to individually discuss their medical condition with a pharmacist wound up taking 13 percent fewer medications on a daily basis and had 60 percent fewer medication-related problems.

43

Wipe, Don't Blow

Wiping your nose is something you were supposed to outgrow as a child. You were probably encouraged from a young age to blow your nose instead. But there is no scientific reason to avoid wiping your nose, and there are good reasons to avoid blowing it.

University of Arizona microbiologist Charles Gerba knows germs. He studies how we spread them to each other and to ourselves.

Handkerchiefs, for example, are an ideal germ spreader. "Organisms persist from one load of laundry to the next, so if you're washing hankies in one load, you're actually blowing your nose on everything you wear, from one load to the next," Dr. Gerba says. Hot water in the laundry will reduce the effect.

But even if you are just blowing your nose into a tissue, "You are spreading virus-laden mucus into the sinuses, causing inflammation."

Dr. Gerba's advice: "The less dramatic the response, the better." When it comes to your nose, "Let it run, and wipe it on a tissue, and you will not be expending energy to share your germs with others or to share them with yourself." We need to realize, he says, "that a nose is really a germ cannon, and there are many good reasons to avoid trying to set it off."

Scientists at the University of Virginia found that the more people with colds blew their noses, the longer their colds lasted. Wiping their noses, on the other hand, caused no worsening of the cold.

44

Common Chores Can Be Dangerous

There are probably few things that seem less dramatic than guiding a lawn mower back and forth across a yard. But lawn mowers are capable of slicing not just grass but nearly anything they come into contact with, including hands and feet. Never let a boring task distract you from the importance of safety.

Michael McReynolds works hard to keep his yard in good shape and has spent more than his share of weekend afternoons mowing the lawn. But as a nurse aboard the Michigan-based Survival Flight program, which transports critically injured patients to the hospital, he's also seen devastating injuries that can come from lawn mowing.

"A lawn mower used carelessly or without proper safety precautions is very dangerous," he warns. "But the vast majority of lawn mower injuries are preventable."

One of the first things Michael does before he cuts the lawn is pick up lose debris on the lawn, especially since his children sometimes leave their toys around the yard. "Any clutter left lying around the yard can fly up into the engine and be projected out the side, almost like a missile, and it can cause serious injury," Michael says.

Personal protective equipment is also a must, according to Michael. To prevent injury, he suggests that everyone who operates a lawn mower wear pants, steel-toed boots, and goggles. In addition, Michael suggests using some form of hearing protection, since lawn mowers, at an average of 95 decibels, are extremely loud.

The single biggest danger, though, is the lawn mower blade. "You should never reach under a lawn mower for any reason. Even when the mower's turned off, the blade is still turning and there's still the risk of a severe injury," says Michael. "And even if there are times when you just want to adjust the height of the mower's wheels, you should pull out the spark plug to ensure that there's no way for the lawn mower to turn on."

University of Michigan researchers found that 75,000 Americans are injured every year in lawn mower accidents.

45

Let Your Stress Out

To appear strong, we often try to hide our struggles. But keeping our problems locked within us only serves to isolate us from people who care about us and who want to help or comfort us. The less willing you are to share your problems with loved ones and friends, the more those problems will come to overwhelm you—and the greater effect those problems will have on your life and your health.

Pete is an employment counselor who helps people who have been downsized out of their jobs. Over time, Pete and his industry in general have expanded their focus from job skills and placement services to the status of the job seekers themselves. "We recognized the incredible stress this situation can create. And we really have to deal with the person and their feelings, or all the training in the world isn't going to see them through to their next job."

According to Pete, "Job seekers and their partners tend to fall into certain emotional patterns after the job loss. Job seekers often feel embarrassed and defensive about being unemployed and may act guarded and withdrawn. They might not want to talk about the search for fear of worrying their partner."

Partners, for their part, "often try to keep a lid on their own worries. When a job seeker becomes uncommunicative, the partner often becomes anxious, wanting to know exactly what he or she is doing to find work. Now they are both keeping everything bottled up, and it can really become debilitating to their lives, their health, their existence."

Instead, Pete says, "Communication is the key to making it through tough times. Open, well-organized, and active families generally do best in weathering a job loss because they can be honest about what they are going through and share both the difficulty and the recovery from it. Be up front with friends and relatives. It's something that can make you or break you, and there's no advantage to going it alone."

Men who cope with stress by talking about their problems and frustrations and confiding in colleagues and friends rather than bottling things up have higher sperm counts than those who do not, according to research findings from a University of Missouri study.

46

No TV During Dinner

In many households there is a constant guest for dinner: television. When television and eating go together, they encourage our overconsumption of both. Separate your television time from your eating time to encourage healthy habits with both.

"I noticed it affected not just what I ate but how much I ate," Debra said of watching television while she ate dinner with her son. "When you are watching television and eating, neither is your real focus. So you can just get lost in a program and not stop yourself from eating too much. Or get lost in eating and not stop yourself from watching too much TV."

And she noted, "You'll eat anything—the worst things—with the television on. It's cookies and snacks and quick-fix meals." She compares it to hanging around with the wrong friends in school. "You'll do things you wouldn't otherwise do, and for no good reason."

When she decided to make a change, Debra not only cut down on what she ate and what she watched but also eliminated the combination. "We have completely changed everything in my approach," she says, "and it really lets you appreciate more what you're doing."

Each meal eaten in front of the television adds up to an hour of time to daily television watching, according to a study by Cincinnati Children's Hospital.

47

Study Your Sports Drink

For exercise lasting forty-five minutes or less, there is no real advantage to drinking anything other than water. For particularly rigorous exercise, a sports drink might help you replenish yourself. You must study the labels, however, because some sports drinks are closer to junk food than nutrition.

꩜ ꩜ ꩜

Tim Dunn is a doctor and a weekend warrior in a local basketball league. He knows firsthand the dilemma facing active people when they reach for a beverage.

"Drinks containing carbohydrates, protein, caffeine, herbal products, vitamins, all claim to be the perfect sports drink. So how can a person choose the sports drink that is right for them?

"That's simple. There is no magic tonic that is going to make you jump higher, run faster, increase your brain power, or transform you into an elite athlete. The purposes of sports drinks are to keep your body hydrated and to replace fluids that you lose during exercise."

Dr. Dunn adds, "Keep in mind that the best source for fluid replacement is water. It's what comprises most of our bodies.

Water is abundant and inexpensive and has been endorsed by Mother Nature for millions of years as the number one drink. Water should be our primary beverage for fluid replacement. However, during intense activities, or activities that last longer than forty-five minutes, water may not be enough."

But what should be in your sports drink?

According to Dr. Dunn, "The optimal sports drink should contain no more than 8 percent carbohydrates. Try to avoid sports drinks that are carbonated, contain caffeine or herbal remedies, and are more than 8 percent sugar. These ingredients may decrease the objective of the sports drink, which is to hydrate the body. Keep it simple. Hydrate yourself, but understand there's no magic in sports drinks. The only thing that is going to make you perform and feel better is a sound diet, plenty of rest, and an appropriate amount of exercise."

Colorado State University researchers have found that for more than nine in ten people, water is the best beverage to drink for their typical exercise activity. Sports drinks are beneficial only for those athletes who participate in high-endurance activities.

48

In Sickness and in Health

Married people tend to imitate each other's health habits. Thus, when you vow to stay together in sickness and in health, it is often the case that you will both be in sickness or in health at the same time. A successful health plan, therefore, factors in not just you but also those closest to you.

When Samantha and Andy were married, she had a vision of living happily ever after in the perfect house. "Those first few months were challenging," Samantha says. "Getting to really know each other and fitting our lives and living habits together. Trying to make the house we bought livable. It was hardly perfect, but it was still wonderful. But before the year was over, all those little challenges seemed meaningless."

Samantha and Andy both began to feel sick, weak, and tired and had lost their appetite. Instead of feeling better a few days later as they expected, the feeling just stayed with them. Samantha went to see a doctor first. Her doctor had no answer for her. Andy tried to tough it out, but he too went to see a doctor, complaining of nearly the same symptoms as Samantha. Unfortunately, his doctor gave him the same inconclusive answer.

The mystery finally began to unravel when Andy drove Samantha to a third doctor. With Andy sitting by Samantha's side, it was obvious to the doctor that they were both in need of care. When she heard the common symptoms, the doctor began asking about Andy and Samantha's common habits—something that was happening to the two of them that might produce this reaction. After ruling out a variety of factors, the doctor seized on the possibility that their house was making them sick. Specifically, the doctor suspected their efforts to fix up the walls had exposed them to remnants of decades-old lead paint—leaving them both with lead poisoning.

Armed with information on the dangers of old paint chips, Andy and Samantha both took precautions in working on their home and began to feel like their old selves again. "But if Andy hadn't been there with me at the doctor's, I don't think we could have found the answer. The fact that this was happening to both of us was a big medical clue."

A survey by researchers at Brigham Young University found that the wife of a man in good health is five times more likely to be healthy than the wife of a man in poor health.

49

Remember, Ginkgo Biloba Won't Help Your Memory

Extract from leaves of the ginkgo biloba tree is marketed world-wide as an enhancer of memory and other mental functions. In the United States alone, $500 million worth is sold every year. Controlled scientific experiments, however, fail to back up the marketing claims.

You're in a shopping center, and you forget where you parked the car. You're on your way to work and you can't remember if you locked the door. You're watching a movie and you can't remember where you've seen the actor before.

"Don't worry. It's normal," says David Salmon, University of California, San Diego, neuropsychologist. "Especially as we get older, our brains just work less efficiently. Things we could remember effortlessly when we were younger require more effort when we get older."

But it's not hopeless. "Any kind of preoccupation or stress makes it difficult to pay attention and have deep memory encoding," says Larry Squire, a professor of psychiatry at the University of California, San Diego. "How well you pay attention at the time of learning information determines how well you will remember it."

Adds Dr. Salmon, "Don't look to ginkgo biloba and other supplements to enhance your memory. The Center for Science in the Public Interest reviewed the research and concluded they're a waste of money."

Using an experimental setup in which half the participants took ginkgo biloba and half took a placebo, the Memory Clinic in Bennington, Vermont, found that there were no measurable differences between the two groups' memories or mental functions.

50

Laughter Really Is Medicine

Laughter helps us deal with pain and difficulties and is valuable in a medical context because it reduces our anxiety and our body's state of alarm. Take time out when you are sick or worried about your health to watch your favorite comedy or read your favorite amusing book.

Dr. Steve Allen Jr. is a family physician and medical professor at the State University of New York. He has lectured for two decades about the role of humor in healing. He is the son of the late actor and humorist Steve Allen Sr.

Dr. Allen has been known to tell jokes and juggle to help calm his patients or even while presenting information to other doctors. Dr. Allen says that laughter has benefits for both health and life in general. "It helps people learn better, become more creative, and resolve conflicts. And it makes people feel a lot better."

Research backs up Dr. Allen's beliefs.

Steven Sultanoff, former president of the Association for Applied and Therapeutic Humor, says studies show laughter seems to increase antibodies that fight upper respiratory diseases and other infections. It lowers serum cortisol, which the body releases under stress. Humor also increases tolerance to pain, which is why Dr. Sultanoff always listens to a funny tape when he drives to the dentist.

"We know the way we think is directly related to the way we feel," Dr. Sultanoff says. "People can think themselves into being depressed, anxious, or angry. But with humor, we shift negative thinking, and it becomes positive thinking."

Researchers at the University of Maryland, Baltimore County, found that people who laughed the least were 40 percent more likely to suffer from heart disease than people who laughed most frequently.

51

Use Caution when Combining Remedies

Many medications are safe and effective when taken alone but ineffective or counterproductive when taken in combination with something else. When taking over-the-counter medication, remember that the effects of a drug must be understood in light of everything else you are taking. When taking prescription medicine, make sure your doctor is aware of all your medications. And it is a good idea to fill all your prescriptions at the same pharmacy because your pharmacist will be able to track all the medications you are taking and alert you if any might counteract each other.

A survey by the National Consumers League found that almost half of the people questioned said they had knowingly exceeded the recommended dose of over-the-counter pain relievers. Fewer than 20 percent said they had read the label completely.

These findings alarm consumer groups and health officials, who note that most of the 175 million Americans who take over-the-counter painkillers every year are unaware of their potential hazards. As a result, experts say, many people misuse these enormously popular drugs, which are used to treat ailments from headaches, arthritis, and viruses to muscle pain.

Health officials emphasize that the most popular over-the-counter pain relievers, including aspirin, acetaminophen, ibuprofen, and naproxen, are safe if used as directed. The problem is that many Americans take the aggressively marketed pills thoughtlessly, "popping these things like they're candy," in the words of liver specialist Dr. William Lee.

Dr. Lee points to a popular flu relief medication that warns patients not to take more than four doses in a twenty-four-hour period. "What it doesn't say is that just as dangerous as taking a fifth dose would be to combine the flu medicine with any number of popular pain relievers. And that's what we see far too much of—products that warn you what not to do with that particular product but ignore the strong possibility that you might be taking something else at the same time."

People who take aspirin regularly to help prevent heart attacks may void its effectiveness by regularly taking other common pain relievers such as ibuprofen, according to doctors at the University of Iowa.

52

Teeth Whitening May Cause Discomfort

A word of caution to those who want to brighten their smile by whitening their teeth. Many people will feel an uncomfortable sensitivity after using at-home whitening products. Consult with your dentist to determine if whitening is appropriate, especially if you have fillings, crowns, or receding gums.

The desire for bright smiles is the latest trend in cosmetic dentistry. In fact, tooth whitening is the most requested cosmetic dental procedure, according to the American Academy of Cosmetic Dentistry.

"Consumer demand for tooth whitening has grown by 300 percent in the past five years," says Wisconsin dentist Christian Kammer.

Besides that, new over-the-counter products, such as whitening strips, paint-on gels, and toothpastes, seem to hit the market every week, boosting annual sales of the tooth-whitening industry into the billions of dollars.

"The bleaching process is inhibited by plaque and tartar buildup, so teeth need to be completely clean before beginning the process," Dr. Kammer notes.

There are important differences between whitening procedures performed by a dentist and those you can do at home. In-office bleaching procedures using either hydrogen or carbamide peroxide, for example, typically cost $350 to $600, while custom-made teeth trays prepared by a dentist for home use run about half that. Over-the-counter products, which contain solutions with weaker peroxide concentrations than those dispensed by dentists, cost between $15 and $40.

"For folks who just want to dabble with whitening, these store-purchased kits can work, but they're not as effective—or as strong—as what patients can get in a dental office," Dr. Kammer says. Inappropriate use of over-the-counter bleaching products also can cause significant damage to tooth enamel, he warns.

A University of Southern California study found that after one week of at-home whitening treatments, 54 percent of patients reported mild sensitivity, 8 percent reported moderate sensitivity, and 4 percent reported severe sensitivity.

53

Maintain Your Sense of Control

The greater your sense of control over what you are doing, the less wear and tear you will put on your body. That does not mean that you can simply choose to be healthy or live a problem-free life. It does mean that by focusing on solutions to the problems that arise, you can keep your attention on what you can do in a given situation instead of what you can't.

When he didn't get promoted, Dean fell into a negative spiral. "I was in this kind of funk," Dean said. He felt discombobulated. Out of sorts. "I was just sitting around. I couldn't focus on anything," Dean said.

With the disappointment at work came a challenge to his commitment to healthy habits. "I was basically saying to myself, 'Life is short. Maybe I should start enjoying myself. Why bother doing all the work to lose weight and try to be healthy when I have no direction?'"

Nutritionist Ann Norris says life difficulties can overwhelm and undermine health goals. "Consumption of high-fat comfort foods can rise as much as 80 percent when people lose their job or have difficulties on the job," she says.

"Something bad happens to them, and people may think losing weight right now or being healthy is insignificant in the scheme of things. But it can actually be even more important because it gives them something to focus on that they can control."

Ann explains, "Exercise helps us deal with both physical and psychological stressors by blunting effects of defensive chemicals produced in our body during times of grief and worry." She warns against giving in to temptation. "It will only heighten your sense that things are out of control. Putting limits on yourself, on the other hand, is a step toward demonstrating control over yourself—and the first step toward feeling in control overall."

Participants in a study who were subjected to a loud noise and told the sound would go away if they succeeded on a test showed fewer effects of stress than those who were told the sound would continue regardless of what they did. Researchers at Pennsylvania State University concluded that a sense of control calmed the first group, even though neither group in fact had any control over the process.

54

Have an Orange

Vitamin C, found in many fruits, including oranges, inhibits the process of artery clogging and lowers blood pressure. Regular consumption of vitamin C has been found to reduce the risk of heart attack, stroke, and premature death.

John was raised on a citrus farm in southwest Texas. He remembers the best and the worst of the farming experience, from the bumper crops to the tree-scorching droughts.

The farm had been in his family for generations, but when it was time for him to choose a career, he decided to leave the farm and become a teacher. At school he used the farm as an example in all sorts of lessons, from math to science. "There was so much that could be learned from the example," John said. He also reminded his students to eat oranges—just about the healthiest food he could think of.

While his father continued to run the farm, John helped out when he could. Then the worst disaster that can befall a citrus farmer struck—freeze. A rare cold snap came through and killed all the trees. John's father was heartbroken and decided to retire from the farming business.

While he was worried over what would become of the farm, John was not ready to give up teaching. He decided to do both, and he took over running the farm. "I'm doing two things I value. In different ways, both contribute to people's lives and help meet their basic needs."

Each ounce of vitamin C–laden fruits consumed per day reduces the risk of premature death by 10 percent, according to doctors at Cambridge University.

55

Build Your Energy Level Gradually

If you get tired easily, remember that improving your energy level can take some time. Whether an underlying medical condition or an overwhelmingly busy life brings on fatigue, practical strategies can increase your stamina. But improvement will not be as easy as flipping a switch. Endurance is built slowly over time.

"Fatigue is a symptom that challenges doctors. It is hard to define because it can feel different for each individual," says Dr. John Francis. "Fatigue is perplexing because it can accompany many different physical ailments, and it can also be related to anxiety, depression, not enough sleep, too much sleep, lack of exercise, too much exercise, or stress."

Dr. Francis says that to understand a patient's fatigue, a physician will usually proceed like a detective, getting as much information about the symptoms and medical history as possible and then following leads and exploring possibilities.

Dr. Francis offers his patients three steps toward greater energy, all of them focused on building slowly toward an improvement. "You should exercise, but do it gradually. Start slowly so you don't increase your fatigue, and try to build up to twenty or thirty minutes of activity per day. You should seek to set a manageable and even pace in your work and daily activities. In other words, set priorities and manage your time and energy efficiently. And you should practice good sleep habits. Establish a ritual for going to bed. Don't take work to bed, don't consume too much caffeine from coffee, teas, colas, and chocolate, and maintain a firm time for going to bed and waking up. Then, step by step, you can improve your energy level."

In a University of Minnesota study of those who complained of frequent fatigue, immediate improvements were rarely seen, but gradual lifestyle changes improved energy levels for nine out of ten participants.

56

Pleasant Smells Boost Your Health

Our senses communicate to our brain whether we should be in a state of alarm or a state of calm. Even when we are in distress in our lives, soothing our senses helps to soothe our system. Surround yourself with pleasant smells when you feeling ill or stressed, and your system will be calmed.

Before a magnetic resonance imaging exam, David, an MRI technologist, brings out his secret weapons.

He displays a black case with an eclectic collection of CDs: Beethoven, James Taylor, Yanni, Frank Sinatra, Eurythmics, Alanis Morissette. As you lie on the scanning table, he pops your choice into a CD player. Soon the music wafts through your headphones. Then he covers your eyelids with an aromatherapy eye pillow scented with a few drops of cucumber or lavender essential oils.

Peacefully, patients are introduced to the MRI process.

The music may not completely drown out the machine's loud bangs, but it and the scent can help you tune out the stress and anxiety during what some consider an unsettling and claustrophobic experience.

An increasing number of health-care providers say they're using these and other methods to help patients banish anxiety during diagnostic tests and before surgery. His co-workers on the radiology staff have found that to be true, David said. The number of patients who cannot tolerate an MRI has decreased since the music option was offered several years ago. That number has dropped further since the department began providing aromatherapy.

A study of women in labor by Oxford University found that aromatherapy—surrounding the patient with pleasant smells—relaxed women and helped them feel in control of their pain. Over 80 percent of women rated the aromatherapy effective in helping them through even the most painful moments of labor.

57

Cherish Your Friends

When we think about safeguarding our health, we generally think in terms of activities—exercising, eating right, getting enough sleep. But an often-overlooked component of good health is quality of relationships with friends and family. People who enjoy good, strong relationships are healthier because they feel less stress generally and tend to deal with stressful situations better. Cherishing your ties to family and friends is as important to your health as good nutrition and exercise.

Leila is a nurse. She knows how to spot danger signs that indicate someone's health is at risk, and she spends part of her work week trying to educate people about the warning signs they should be looking for in their family, friends, and neighbors.

"People think in terms of having enough food, and proper shelter. When something is wrong there, we think we will immediately recognize it. But no one sees loneliness. It doesn't happen when we are there checking in; it happens when we're not looking."

Leila has seen signs of loneliness across age groups, from senior citizens who have outlived their friends to young people who feel left out or misunderstood.

Leila explains that loneliness is a condition with tremendous implications, not just for how we feel about ourselves, but for how we treat ourselves. "A lonely person is more likely to skip meals or, when eating, to eat less healthy foods. A lonely person is more likely to avoid getting medical care when they are sick, and to ignore or forget to take medication. A lonely person is just willing to accept a lower standard of life for themselves."

"Whether you are concerned about a lonely person, or a lonely person yourself," Leila says, "the best thing you can do is show someone you care. As soon as you crack that isolation that comes from feeling left out, feeling that no one cares, you begin to see people treating themselves better. Loneliness is a feeling, but it can be replaced by a better feeling."

Loneliness in otherwise healthy people was associated with increased blood pressure and decreased heart capacity, according to doctors at the University of Chicago.

58

Secondhand Smoke Affects the Brain

We tend to think of smoking and polluted air as threats to our lungs. They are that, but they also compromise our circulatory system, affecting how our heart and brain function. Secondhand smoke reduces not only blood flow but also our ability to think clearly.

ஏ ஏ ஏ

Eve was never fond of secondhand smoke. But when the Tampa resident became a mother, her interest in the subject grew. "It's the kind of thing you hear about a lot but that people don't really understand."

What Eve learned shocked her. "Here we have this known risk factor for developing all kinds of diseases, for weakening different functions of the body, from your lungs to your heart to your teeth even. And it's all around us—in places we work and eat."

Eve's concern grew; she knew that she could protect her family but that many people, especially children, were needlessly exposed to this risk.

Inspired by studies showing the effects of secondhand smoke on children's learning, she decided to form a group to work against secondhand smoke exposure. Activists from across Florida joined in her efforts. They decided to mount a citizens' petition to place a question on the ballot to ban smoking in restaurants and workplaces.

One of their brochures, "Secondhand Smoke, Think About It," emphasized the connection between secondhand smoke and the brain.

When the question finally made the ballot, it was passed in a landslide. "It's time to protect ourselves, our families, each other," Eve says.

Cincinnati Children's Hospital found that 85 percent of children have measurable exposure to secondhand smoke. These children were found to have lower scores on standardized reading, logic, and math tests than children who had not been exposed to secondhand smoke.

59

Don't Pack like a Mule

Travelers often load themselves down with heavy baggage and plow ahead with little concern about how their habits affect their bodies. People were not meant to move vast quantities of luggage, especially slung over their shoulder.

"Shoulders take more wear and tear today than ever before. Toting travel bags, luggage, laptop computers, backpacks, sports equipment, and musical instruments places stress on the shoulders that can lead to muscle strain and lower back pain," explains Dr. Vernon Tolo, president of the American Academy of Orthopaedic Surgeons.

The American Academy of Orthopaedic Surgeons has found that four out of five adults experience lower back pain and that problems caused by the lower back are the most frequent cause of lost work days in adults under the age of forty-five.

"The best treatment for shoulder stress and strain is prevention," Dr. Tolo says. "Increasing muscle strength in your shoulders and daily stretching are essential, but selecting the right shoulder packs and using them properly are equally important. The right pack lightens the load and reduces the stress." Dr.

Tolo recommends that people take advantage of luggage with wheels and bags made out of lightweight material. "But if you must carry, make sure you walk in an upright position and don't allow the bag to pull you to one side."

The American Academy of Orthopaedic Surgeons recommends that you not carry more than 15 percent of your body weight on your shoulders and back.

60

Have Some Tea with Your Remodeling

Remodeling efforts, including any painting or gluing, generally result in an unhealthy buildup of chemicals in the home. Dry tea bags will absorb chemicals in the air and reduce the amount of time it takes for a home to regain healthy air quality.

Serena fell in love with a very old house in central Philadelphia. It needed plenty of attention, Serena thought, but she just couldn't resist it. After buying it, she made her way through it one room at a time—patching, painting, refinishing the hardwood floors, putting in new moldings and fixtures.

Serena said, "I loved the old-style design of the house, but there's something to be said for walls without holes in them and an update on fifty-year-old faded paint."

Unfortunately for Serena, the fumes and smells produced by her efforts were hard to deal with. "It smelled like I lived in a factory or a refinery. And since I started one room after I finished the last, it seemed like fumes had become the permanent scent of the house."

While she left the windows open as much as possible, that was not the most attractive solution during Philadelphia winters. "You could either air out the place and freeze, or keep the place warm while you choked on the air."

Then Serena read about the tea bag solution. "Tea bags are porous and soak up what's around them. Now I spread tea bags throughout the room I'm working in. Much of the stink goes right into the bags. I would say it cuts in half the time it takes for a room to stop smelling of paint and varnish."

The only challenge for Serena is putting up with the strange look she gets at the supermarket when she buys twenty boxes of tea.

Researchers at the Tokyo Metropolitan Consumer Center found that scattering tea bags throughout a newly remodeled room reduced the toxicity level of chemicals in the air by up to 90 percent.

61

Short-Term Stress Is Healthy

Our bodies are designed to deal with short-term stress. When we are under stress, adrenaline surges within us and our immune system is heightened. Short-term stress, such as having to give a speech, has a defined endpoint, and afterward the adrenaline surge can stop and the body can return to normal. Long-term stress, on the other hand, such as being overwhelmed by one's job, has no defined endpoint, and the state of constant alarm that the body is forced into weakens the immune system and compromises the body's defenses.

The season for a professional football player is only sixteen games long. While each game lasts about three hours, the actual time spent on the field with the ball in play amounts to no more than about six minutes per game. That means a star player's season is based on success in just over an hour and a half of effort spaced out over four months. And even a Hall of Fame career can take as little as ten hours of actual in-game action.

Of course, countless hours of practice and conditioning take place before those games begin, but the measure of an athlete will be performance in those games. How do these athletes deal with the incredible weight of having to give an outstanding performance in such a limited amount of time?

"That is really the positive side of stress," says psychologist Gary Foley. "We are all capable of doing more than we imagine in short bursts."

Gary adds, "The key, though, is that they are short bursts. If you asked a football player who won a game on Sunday to come back and do it again on Monday, he would have trouble showing up to the game, much less playing in it. If you asked him to come play seven days a week, he would collapse before the week was out."

Gary explains, "Short bursts of effort are healthy stressors. They focus us and bring out of us the best we have. They are not just productive; they are healthy. It puts the body through its paces. It's good for the circulation system. Good for the immune system. And it's good for just a little bit at a time."

Researchers at the University of Michigan found that short-term stress boosts the body's ability to fight disease. However, prolonged stress weakens the immune system by as much as 60 percent.

62

Keep Bugs Away
with DEET-Based Products

Countless products boast of their prowess as bug repellents. Products with DEET, the trade name for the chemical diethyltoluamide, however, have been found to be uniquely capable of repelling bugs for a lasting period and after just one application. DEET was originally developed by U.S.D.A. scientists to protect soldiers from bug bites.

Everett Martin is an entomologist. In common language, he studies bugs. "It's a good conversation starter. When I tell people what I do, they all have questions. Insects are all around us, but we don't give them that much thought."

One question he gets all the time is how to reduce insect bites. It's a concern about more than just preventing annoyance, Everett realizes. Mosquitoes, for example, can carry countless diseases, with devastating consequences for humans. Everett has studied the behavior of humans and bugs and has concluded that a strategy can work.

To prevent insect bites, people should dress in light-colored clothing with long sleeves and pants, avoid being outside during the peak insect periods of dusk and dawn, and use the right kind of insect repellent.

"The best insect repellents don't really repel or kill insects; they distract them. DEET works by confusing mosquitoes and other biting pests' ability to hone in on the carbon dioxide that attracts them to humans and other mammals," Everett says.

"The insects don't disappear—there's nothing that can do that—but they do lose interest for the time being when they can't find a victim."

Products containing DEET produced the fewest mosquito bites in tests run at the University of Florida Entomology Laboratory.

63

Write It Down

Illness can be more than we can handle. One way to help process what's happening without becoming overwhelmed is to write down your thoughts in a personal journal. Writing about our lives helps reduce our stress level and can actually improve our overall health.

Kirk teaches people how to record their thoughts, their feelings, their daily events, or whatever else might be on their minds in a journal. Kirk doesn't work for a school or college; he works for a hospital.

"Writing about illness and traumatic events helps patients to finally deal with and accept what has happened, and that process reduces stress and sleeplessness. Altering the physiological stress patterns in their bodies, improves their health."

Kirk continues, "People need to have a place for personal voice. Writing allows you to find answers to daunting problems within yourself rather than having to rely on answers from others. Through that you get a sense of empowerment."

Whatever type of journal, the rules are the same: there are none. "We all suffer from English major's disease," he says.

"Forget about outlines, grammar, even punctuation. The journal is not about school or grades. It's all for you."

Kirk recommends getting started by setting a timer and writing for at least eight minutes about whatever comes to mind. And it isn't necessary to look at your journal as a daily obligation. "A journal is the kind of friend you want it to be, an everyday phone call or occasional get-together."

A North Dakota State University research project asked people suffering from chronic conditions such as asthma and arthritis to write about their lives in a journal for an hour per week. In the months after they started their journals, 47 percent of the patients showed a measurable improvement in symptoms.

64

Sleep Well

Sleep is fuel for our systems that we cannot do without. As is the case with food and water, we cannot simply skimp for a day and make up for it the next. Our bodies expect a constant supply of sleep, and they function best when provided a full night's sleep every twenty-four hours.

Military leaders have identified a long-ignored but very important threat to soldiers: lack of sleep. Lieutenant Colonel Jim Chartier, commander of the Marine First Tank Battalion, called sleep deprivation "our biggest enemy. It makes easy tasks difficult."

"We don't ever want to go down the road of no sleep," says Air Force sleep researcher John Caldwell.

"There is simply no substitute for it," adds Colonel Gregory Belenky, the army's chief scientist.

Brain scans show that a missed night of sleep will cause a metabolic drop of 12 percent to 14 percent in the prefrontal cortex, the section of the brain responsible for higher-order reasoning and judgment. For soldiers and pilots, that means the part of the brain that discerns friend from foe, chooses targets, and navigates through a battlefield is truly addled by sleep loss. Sleep researchers surmise that friendly-fire incidents, errant convoys, and operating accidents have been caused by fatigue.

"There's good news and there's bad news," says Colonel Belenky. "Troops deprived of sleep for long enough will sleep anywhere, and some sleep—a forty-five-minute catnap in the mud, for instance—is better than no sleep at all. They know they must nap early, nap often."

But that too is the bad news, Colonel Belenky says. "With little sleep, troops can doze off during chemical attacks, while on watch, or while operating dangerous equipment—and in wartime, it is all dangerous equipment."

Colonel Belenky found in his research that a single night without sleep can render a subject slow to react, easy to distract, and very forgetful. "The sleepless subject becomes impulsive, irritable, and unable to respond to complex problems with any but the most rote of responses," he says. Even more alarming, "Without sleep, people have no grasp of the extent of their impairment."

According to the National Sleep Foundation's survey on sleep, 40 percent of adults are so sleepy during the day that it interferes with their daily activities. The foundation reports sleep deprivation triggers a 10 to 35 percent drop in antibodies and immune cells. Sleep is essential for the repair of immune cells. People should aim for at least eight hours of sleep a night and more if they become ill.

65

Your Teeth Are More than Something to Chew On

We think of our teeth as existing in almost a separate medical world from the rest of the body. After all, we go to a dentist for our teeth and a doctor for our body. However, gum diseases can have consequences for the functioning of the entire body. In fact, our teeth and gums are a vitally important gateway to our coronary system. To take care of your body, you must take care of your teeth and gums. Brushing, flossing, and getting regular cleanings and checkups help to defend not only your teeth but your overall well-being.

Dental experts are looking beyond drilling, yanking teeth, and doing root canals to consider the importance of the mouth in assessing one's health. Specifically, they see evidence that identifying mouth microbes provides important clues to general health.

Researchers are learning to detect changes in the huge populations of bacteria, viruses, yeast cells, and other microbes that thrive in the mouth. "These bugs don't colonize your mouth in a random way," said Sigmund Socransky, a professor of periodontology at Harvard University. "Rather, they form communities in a pattern that is dictated by other bugs and by the mouth environment."

After much study, he said, "we're beginning to see what's there. We're cataloging the species. We're now relating them to health and disease, which leads to the next step: suppressing the ones related to disease and encouraging those related to health."

Professor Socransky noted it's a very good thing that certain microbes inhabit the mouth. The healthful bacteria tend to keep the harmful ones at bay, he said. "They are an enormous help to us, in the sense that there are so many pathogenic species that could potentially take that niche and cause disease."

Professor Socransky has shown in his research that shifts in microbe populations accompany disorders ranging from gum disease to heart disease, blood vessel abnormalities, strokes, and pneumonia. The outcome of the combat between bacteria-wielding toxins can influence dental health, he said. There are "good bugs that kill bad bugs. We'd love to replace the bad guys with good guys. But we don't know how to do that just yet."

People with periodontal disease are up to 57 percent more likely to suffer from heart problems, according to a study at the University of Pittsburgh.

66

Home Is Where Accidents Happen

Our homes are comforting to us. They are where we spend most of our time. They are where we feel safest. But because home is so central, it is also where the threat of accidental injuries is highest. Parents of new babies look through their homes to find any potential danger to the baby—anything that might be touched, could fall, or could get in the way. But when children are past a certain age, we stop thinking about potential threats within our home. Look through your house with the eyes you would use to protect a child, and take some precautionary steps to avoid potential accidents in your home.

As Patty approached the front door of her home after completing a few errands, she heard the screech of smoke detectors. Horrified, she realized the electric Christmas candle had fallen from the front window onto the sofa, which was smoldering. She raced inside for the fire extinguisher but was too late. Once the drapes ignited, there was nothing to do but run out and dial 9-1-1.

"As soon as I got outside, the living room windows blew out from the heat," she recalled. "Within fifteen minutes, the fire caused a quarter of a million dollars' worth of damage. I stood there and watched while the house I've lived in for two decades was destroyed."

Patty says, "I realized how slim the margin was for this fire being deadly. If it had happened at night, my whole family would have been in the house. If we didn't have smoke detectors, we might never have made it." Indeed, most fire-related fatalities occur in homes without smoke detectors.

Patty and her family spent a year living in a small apartment while their home was repaired. But now she has made some changes. She has nine smoke detectors and a sprinkler system. She wouldn't dream of leaving a candle in the window. "Why take the chance?" she asks.

A study at the University of North Carolina found that twenty thousand Americans die annually due to accidents within their homes, and another seven million suffer injuries in their homes. Meanwhile, 56 percent of Americans in that study said they had not made a single effort to make their home safer.

67

Value the Multiple Uses of Aspirin

The most common headache relief provider until it was displaced by ibuprofen and acetaminophen, aspirin reduces our susceptibility to blood clots and has been linked to a reduced risk for heart disease and Alzheimer's disease.

🍎 🍎 🍎

"Aspirin can definitely be called a wonder drug, ranked right up there with penicillin. But it is a drug," says Dr. Thomas Cassidy.

"Historically, aspirin was first used as a pain reliever, but why it worked was not known. Now we know that the body reacts to injury by releasing hormonelike substances called prostaglandins, which cause inflammation, redness, swelling, and subsequent pain. Aspirin blocks the enzyme responsible for production of prostaglandins. Aspirin has also been used for decreasing fever and inflammation," Dr. Cassidy says.

"Today, we appreciate the fact that aspirin reduces blood clotting. This was first thought of as a potentially negative side effect, but it is really a tremendous benefit. Decreased clotting aids in the prevention and treatment of strokes."

He continues, "More recently, researchers noticed that people who took even small amounts of aspirin regularly had a decreased risk of heart attacks from coronary artery disease. This was attributed to the effect on clotting. It now appears that reduced inflammation is also an important way in which aspirin decreases heart attacks.

"In fact," Dr. Cassidy adds, "my advice is, if you are a woman over fifty or a man over forty, taking aspirin each day is a valuable step to reducing your susceptibility to major disease."

Elderly people who took aspirin daily for more than two years showed a 55 percent lower rate of dementia in a National Institute on Aging study. The Mayo Clinic reported that taking aspirin every day reduced the rate of heart attacks by 44 percent and of certain kinds of cancer by 50 percent.

68

Religion Can Help Ease Your Burden

What is the difference between those who respond to challenges and those who give up? More than anything else, it is their confidence and sense of purpose. Those who keep going are more likely to believe they will succeed and more likely to believe that what they are doing matters. Whether changing their lives to improve their health or dealing with the recovery from a health problem, people with strong religious beliefs benefit from the foundation of confidence and purpose their beliefs provide.

"We all want to be in control. But when you get to a VA hospital and you've got a foot wound that won't heal, you come to understand you're not in control," says Jon, an air force veteran.

Jon says his solution to seizing control in an uncontrollable situation is turning to his faith. "When you look to your faith, you have far more peace about life."

Dr. Harold Koenig agrees. "Furious attempts to gain control over health conditions breed anxiety and depression. But religious beliefs provide an indirect form of control that helps interrupt the vicious cycle."

Dr. Koenig says the favorable impact religion has on health flows from the greater sense of purpose in life, a sense of control, social support, honorable living, and serenity. "Religious beliefs enable a patient to turn a health situation over to a higher power and stop worrying and obsessing about it," Dr. Koenig says.

Prayer not only "gives patients something to do so they don't feel as helpless" but also can foster relaxation, which helps the body function better. "I think we're discovering that neither religion nor science is enough by itself," Dr. Koenig says. "You need to address the whole person. Not just their body. Not just their psychology. Not just their social or religious aspect. But all of these come together and influence each other, and you need to address the whole to get the best outcome."

A Columbia University study found that people who make religion a significant part of their lives are 81 percent less likely to battle anxiety and depression and are more likely to have confidence that they can recover from an illness.

69

Noise Matters

The requirements of life, such as food, shelter, and safety, also include avoiding oppressively loud noise. Whether you are in the workplace or at home, prolonged exposure to uncomfortable levels of noise will affect your ability to think, your ability to remember, your disposition, and your overall health.

You're sitting in your car at a traffic light as you start to unwind at the end of the workday. Suddenly your vehicle is vibrating from a deafening sound. Your shoulders immediately rise to meet the lobes of your ears. Your heart pounds. And then you turn to see if your partners in traffic have also hunched down in survival mode. Then you see him. The person in the booming car next to you is bopping to the thundering reverberations.

Enter Ted Rueter. No, he's not the fellow conducting the car concert next to you. He is the sound of one hand clapping.

The founder of Noise Free America, he is a mild-mannered political science professor at Tulane University. He walks softly and carries a loud message—at low volume, of course. Professor Rueter gets riled up about boom cars and leaf blowers. He's concerned about your health—and the quality of your environment.

Two years ago, while a professor at the University of California in Los Angeles, Professor Rueter taught a class on political advocacy and activism. In the process of teaching students techniques to bring about social change, he tuned in to the fact that he found Los Angeles "irritatingly noisy."

He was not alone. Fourteen of his students joined the organization he subsequently founded. Today, Noise Free America, a national lobbying group, has twenty-seven local chapters in twenty states. Noise, says the antinoise crusader, lowers sex drive, causes sleep deprivation and depression, "harms cognitive development and language acquisition," and results in hearing loss. Some twenty-eight million Americans have hearing loss, and 10 percent of those cases, Professor Rueter says, are noise induced. Loud noise causes our hearts to beat faster, our pulse rates to go up, our digestive juices to slow down, our blood pressure to rise, "all related to the stress of noise."

Professor Rueter warns, "We are becoming a nation oblivious to noise while suffering the consequences."

Researchers at Cornell found that workers in noisy offices experienced significantly higher levels of stress and made 40 percent fewer attempts to solve a difficult problem they were presented with.

70

Limit Your Exposure to Pesticides

There is a more important consideration than how green your lawn is or how vibrant your flowers are or how big your vegetables are. And that is how much harm the pesticides you use are causing. Pesticides are available to use in your garden because they are deadly to insects and other threats. But their power is also their weakness. Too much exposure to pesticides is not only a threat to pests but a threat to humans, pets, and other creatures. Consider natural alternatives to pesticides.

Robina Suwol was dropping her sons off at school one sunny spring day in Los Angeles when she saw a man wearing a hazardous-materials suit spraying the side of the building. Her sons, Brandon and Nicholas, then ten and six, walked right into a fine mist of what turned out to be pesticide. Nicholas, who suffers from asthma, experienced a severe respiratory attack. That was five years ago.

Through a public records request, Robina found out that school maintenance workers were spraying pesticides and herbicides at levels ten times higher than the manufacturer's recommended dosage.

Robina then founded a nationally recognized program in the Los Angeles Unified School District that alerts parents to the use of chemical sprays on school campuses, allowing them to make alternative arrangements to address their children's needs. Six thousand parents have registered for notification.

"We are nationally renowned for this program now. Other districts are looking at us to change their policy as well," said school board member Julie Korenstein, who was an early champion of Robina's cause.

The National School Pesticide Reform Coalition released a report highlighting the school district's policy as one of twenty-seven exemplary programs around the country. Robina was honored by Environment California for her efforts.

"It's been an effort of love in terms of protecting kids," said Robina, who spends many of her weekends at health fairs spreading the word about pesticides. "I want to help other people so their kids don't get sick."

A study conducted at Emory University found that those who frequently used pesticides at home had a 70 percent higher risk of getting Parkinson's disease.

71

Hostility Hurts You

Positive connections between people are a source of mental and physical well-being. Negative feelings toward those around you are a source of mental and physical strain. Realize that your anger will hurt you more than it will hurt the target of your dismay.

"Maybe real men should eat quiche. They might live longer," says philosophy professor Sam Keen. In the name of better health, Sam argues for a male makeover that replaces violence, materialism, and power with peace, spirituality, and cooperation.

"We still are raised primarily to be warriors," Sam said. "Potency is the mark of a man, but that is a cultural identity that may make us sick with stress."

In his research, Sam became intrigued by the relationship between spirituality and health. Now Sam encourages men to define a sense of self that is independent of cultural expectations. "The more we try to impose our vision on everyone," he said, "the more disappointed we become. That will sicken us."

Sam says too many men adopt values and behaviors that traditionally have been associated with them. He calls for men to "create their own stories" instead of believing the hand-me-down myths about them. "We are biologically aggressive animals, but aggression is different from hostility," he said. "Aggressive means we are energetic beings, and we have to do something with that energy. That energy can be channeled toward making peace as easily as waging war."

Brown Medical School doctors found that people with high levels of hostility were 6 percent more likely to suffer from heart disease.

72

Remember the Drugs We Tend to Forget

What is the single most popular drug in the world? You might make fifty wrong guesses before you hit on it: caffeine. Caffeine alters signaling activity within the brain in a way that is similar to cocaine's. It is also addictive. Yet its use is so widespread in coffee, tea, chocolate, and soda that we conveniently overlook its status as a drug. In low doses, caffeine can have positive effects, and for that reason it is used in some pain relievers. In high doses, however, caffeine can both interfere with sleep and increase blood pressure.

It seems harmless enough. A citrus-flavored powder packed with vitamins, minerals, and a jolt of caffeine. You mix it with water or fruit juice, drink it, and you're off to seize the day.

But because of its popularity with high school–aged student athletes, use of the drink has generated a stir among parents and coaches.

"Caffeine is a stimulant. High concentrations are banned by the NCAA and the International Olympic Committee," says one concerned parent. "This product contains five times the caffeine of a cola drink."

In Nebraska the high school athletic association is weighing the need for a policy to address use of these kinds of products. "We currently have no policies regarding the use of performance-enhancing substances, but recently we began exploring whether to establish one. I'm not naive enough to believe that we don't have our fair share of supplement use in Nebraska," said Jim Tenopir, executive director of the association. "Our perspective is that they should be used only with proper medical authority."

Jim warns, "The biggest danger is that these products can be seen as some kind of magic bullet. Young people, like anyone else, are looking for an edge in sports. They think something they can buy and take will make them better. And in this case, you're sprinkling it in juice, so they think it must be food for them. But there is no evidence to show this will help them, and there have been good reasons that respected sports organizations across the world have banned excessive caffeine consumption in athletes."

The majority of scientific evidence shows that, for a healthy adult, moderate quantities of caffeine (250 to 350 milligrams per day—about three cups of coffee) pose no significant health risks. However, a link between higher amounts of caffeine and certain heart problems, such as arrhythmias, has been reported by doctors at the University of Texas.

73

High Heels Cause Knee Problems

High heels create an unnatural walking challenge, which the body deals with by putting more strain on the knees. The lower your heels, the more prepared your legs are to walk on them.

Dr. Casey Kerrigan's work will be done when women everywhere put health before fashion by chucking their high heels into the garbage. Dr. Kerrigan's research suggests that women's dress shoes—and they don't have to be six-inch heels—may be the leading culprit of knee osteoarthritis in women.

"If we get the word out that it's really bad for you, then hopefully it will go out of fashion," said Dr. Kerrigan, a University of Virginia professor and chair of the department of physical medicine and rehabilitation.

In her research, Dr. Kerrigan used motion analysis and force sensors in the ground to calculate stress on the knees. In recent follow-up studies, Dr. Kerrigan has found that even small heels stress the knees. "We believe something as low as an inch and a half may cause problems. It's not just stilettos; it's even day-to-day sensible women's shoes," Dr. Kerrigan said. "Meanwhile, it's very difficult to find women's shoes with anything less than two-inch heels."

Osteoarthritis is caused when the surface covering of the knee joints degenerates. Over time, as the cartilage breaks down, bones rub together, causing severe pain. "It can be quite serious because it can limit a person's mobility," said Dr. Linda Staiger, University of Virginia's head of the division of general orthopedics. "It makes it difficult to drive, work, even get around in their household if they have steps."

While Dr. Kerrigan recommends that women stick to wearing flats, she's also hard at work designing the perfect shoe.

A University of Virginia study found that when women wear high heels they exert 23 percent more pressure on their knees than when they wear flat shoes, contributing to an overall rate of arthritis in the knee that is twice as great for women as for men.

74

Guilt Is Bad for You

Wallowing in disappointment over something you did is not productive. Not only are you going to mentally exhaust yourself; you can also compromise your body's ability to ward off disease. Carrying the burden of disappointment in yourself or in others is something we choose to do and something we would not do if we had our health in mind.

"One thing there's no shortage of is guilt," says Henry, a counselor who works with people overburdened by the demands of career and family. "An average person with responsibilities at home and at work can spend just about every minute of the day worrying about what she or he won't have time to do.

"Of course," he continues, "the problem with this guilt is that it starts because you don't have enough time to do what needs to be done. Then you waste a good bit of the time you do have feeling bad about not having enough of it."

Henry recommends making a clear distinction between productive time and wasted time. "You need to separate out the time that is contributing neither to your home life nor work life—whether that's time wasted being inefficient or time wasted worrying—and maximize the use of your time for what matters."

Henry adds, "If you are organized, you won't magically be able to create forty-eight-hour days in which you can get everything in the world done. But you will feel the progress as you finish what you set out to finish and move from one thing to another."

Henry also advises us not to make promises we'll have trouble keeping. "If you say you are going to do something, you simply have to do it. Failing to do so will leave you deep in guilt. So be strategic about what you say you are going to do. Think about what you want to commit to, and be realistic about it."

Henry says doing things like this will cut down on the guilt you carry, and carrying guilt is "the least productive thing you can do. It is a burden on your mental health and your physical health."

Feelings of guilt, according to a study by doctors at the University of Hull in England, interfere with the body's production of the antibody immunoglobulin A, which protects against infection.

75

Keep Variety in Mind When Exercising

Exercising for general health is best accomplished by doing a variety of activities. Doctors do not advise taking up only one kind of exercise because doing that will put excessive strain on the muscles needed for that particular exercise while offering little reward to the muscles uninvolved in that exercise. Give yourself some variety to help keep your whole body in shape and to keep yourself interested in what you're doing.

Justine's job is to promote good health habits in members of her company's health plan. When it comes to exercise, she emphasizes the value of playing the field.

"First of all, when something is fun, we are more likely to do it, more likely to stick with it. Imagine how much easier life would be if you looked forward to doing things that you now think of as a burden."

Justine advises people to incorporate other elements of life into their exercise plans. "You may not love exercising, but what if you exercised with a friend? And now that time is not some kind of punishment but a chance to spend time with someone you like. Or for your walk go to a park you've never visited or a town you rarely get to." Steps like these, Justine says, will help you see "your workout as something other than work."

Justine also encourages people to try out as many different exercises as they can. "You will become bored with the same routine over and over again. Try a little bit of everything. Mix your regular walk with a swim, with aerobics, with a team sport. The mix will keep you interested and is better for your body."

Justine continues, "If time is limited, shorter workouts are better than no exercise at all, but challenge yourself to increase the duration or intensity of your exercise for one workout session each week." She cautions, "Don't overdo, though, and as you exercise, keep a record of your goals and reward yourself as you improve your fitness level."

Doctors at University Hospital in Innsbruck, Austria, studied men who exercised exclusively by bicycling. Because of the pressure placed on the small seating area of the bicycles, nearly 90 percent of the riders studied had low sperm counts.

76

Don't Use Fireworks

They're sold in stores in many states and may seem safe to handle. But personal fireworks are the most dangerous entertainment product available. Save yourself from the threat of devastating accidents, and limit your contact with fireworks to viewing professional displays.

Once he thought of them as little more than a loud toy. Then Frank lost three fingers from his left hand to fireworks.

"An exploding firecracker can devastate a person's life in a flash," said Frank. "Fireworks should be off limits to all except qualified personnel. Under no circumstances should children play with firecrackers or related devices—the risk is too great."

Frank continues, "Firecrackers can misfire. The fuse may be defective. A wind shift might change the rocket's direction or what seems to be a dud suddenly explodes." Even sparklers, which may appear to be safe for young children, burn at very high temperatures and can easily ignite clothing.

Frank has testified before state health committees on the sale and use of fireworks, and he travels every spring to schools to show children firsthand the danger of firecrackers.

"Children need to be supervised by adults at all times during Independence Day events. Children cannot assess the potential danger involved and cannot act appropriately in case of emergency."

He tells everyone he can one simple truth about using fireworks. Holding up his left hand, he says, "It's not worth it."

Hospitals treat an estimated twenty-five thousand fireworks-related injuries every year in the United States, according to the U.S. Consumer Product Safety Commission. The total medical and other expenses associated with these injuries add up to more than $350 million per year.

77

Do You Work in a Sick Building?

Buildings with inadequate ventilation can trap poor-quality air inside a building while recirculating viruses and contaminants throughout. If you regularly feel ill at work, find out everything you can about your building's ventilation system.

"There's not a lot you can do in a modern building with windows that don't open," laments Joe Stearns, who has both worked in and studied the air quality of office buildings. "We got too good at sealing off a building. We thought it would be wonderful for reducing heating and cooling costs. But it is also wonderful for trapping things we don't want inside the building."

Joe says the culprits include chemical contaminants from indoor sources such as adhesives, carpeting, upholstery, manufactured wood products, copy machines, pesticides, and cleaning agents, all of which emit volatile organic compounds. In low levels these compounds can cause acute reactions in some people. However, high concentration may lead to chronic health problems. Chemical contaminants from outdoor sources, such as vehicle exhaust, plumbing vents, and building exhausts, can also plague a building by entering through ill-placed air-intake vents.

"Your company should be monitoring the air quality in the building. If there is a problem, the company should be open about the condition and the steps being taken to resolve it."

Joe adds, "At the individual level, though, you can help the air quality in your office with plants. NASA did scientific research that proved foliage and flowering plants have the ability to clear the air of these pollutants and help with sick building syndrome and improve indoor air quality." Joe recommends philodendron, diffenbachia, azalea, bamboo palm, corn plant, chrysanthemum, poinsettia, golden pothos, and spider plant.

The World Health Organization estimates that nearly 30 percent of office buildings worldwide contain poor air quality.

78

Stay Safe in the Sun

Skin cancer is the most common form of cancer, occurring in more than 1 million Americans annually. Sun exposure and sunburn represent the leading preventable cause of both the most deadly form of skin cancer, melanoma, and the most common forms, basal cell and squamous cell carcinomas. Protect your skin when you're in the sun as you would protect yourself from any serious threat.

Which states' residents are most likely to get sunburned? You would probably guess Florida or California or a state known for its sunny days. In fact, the highest rates of sunburn are found in Colorado, Iowa, Michigan, Indiana, and Wyoming. "It seems to come down to sun-safe behaviors. The people in those states face fewer sun-oriented events such as beach going and may not be taking sun safety seriously," says dermatologist Timothy M. Johnson of the University of Michigan.

"While most people know that the sun's rays are dangerous, that does not always translate into recognizable protective actions," says Dr. Johnson. "Wearing sunscreen and practicing sun-safe behavior can protect against not only sunburn, but also premature aging and the future development of skin cancer."

Dr. Johnson continues, "Sun protection habits are especially important at a young age since 80 percent of a person's lifetime sun damage occurs before the age of eighteen." He adds, "Early sun protection behaviors by parents, and consistent use throughout life, may decrease a child's lifetime risk of developing melanoma."

Dr. Johnson says that while it's important to practice sun safety, it's even more important to practice it correctly. "Studies have shown that sunscreen users do not apply enough sunscreen in a single application to adequately protect the whole body. Consequently, the SPF achieved will be considerably less than that expected and in many cases will be closer to half of that indicated by the product label."

The bottom-line advice from Dr. Johnson is: "Use an SPF of at least 15, and use sunscreen any time you are going to be out in the sun for more than twenty minutes. Apply the sunscreen thirty minutes before you go outside. Pay a lot of attention to putting the sunscreen on your face, ears, hands, and arms, and reapply every two hours or immediately after swimming."

National Cancer Institute surveys of more than 150,000 respondents found that 32 percent of Americans had been sunburned within the previous twelve months. Among those under eighteen, the rate was 80 percent. Exposure to sunburn triples the lifetime risk of skin cancer.

79

Don't Take Falling Down Lightly

Most people worry more about the rare and awful things that might occur than the common, more likely threats. Conditioning both your body and your surroundings to make falling down a less likely occurrence is one of the most significant steps you can take to protect your health.

Working in his Locomotion Research Laboratory at Virginia Tech, Professor Thurmon Lockhart is determined to solve the mystery of falling down.

"Falls are a looming threat, especially with age. The average person's life will be seriously affected by a fall. What I want to find out is why these falls happen and how we can prevent them."

In his laboratory, Professor Lockhart is suiting up young and old volunteers in a harness and a network of sensors that test musculoskeletal and neuromuscular changes and biomechanical responses during slips and recoveries.

As a test subject walks back and forth along an experimental platform in Lockhart's lab, the sensors monitor muscle and joint activities in the feet, ankles, legs, hips, and arms. At a randomly chosen moment in the test, a student assistant secretly pours a slippery solution of liquid detergent and water behind the subject. On the way back, the subject slips and goes through the motions of trying to maintain his or her balance (a harness prevents the subject from actually falling).

All the data from the monitoring sensors is fed into a computer model, providing information to the researchers about the subject's gait while walking and the body motions involved during slipping and recovery. Lockhart and his students are running tests on a group of volunteers ranging in age from eighteen to over sixty-five.

There's more to Lockhart's study than investigating the mechanics of walking, slipping, and recovering, however. "Another important factor is understanding the changes to gait and balance brought about by aging," he said. For example, as people age their walking gait tends to change. "We may take slower and shorter steps, making higher impact with our heels—which in turn seems to make slipping more likely." Also as we age, Lockhart noted, sensory factors such as vision, inner ear, and touch sensitivity decline. "These changes make us less able to detect that we're slipping until it's too late."

Researchers at Virginia Tech have found that falling is the second leading cause of accidental death among those over the age of forty-five and the leading cause of accidental death among those over the age of seventy-five.

80

Limit Your Piercings

The lower earlobe is the least dangerous area of the body to have pierced. Other places on the ear contain cartilage, which has a lower blood flow and will heal less quickly than the lobe.

"Half the body piercings done in this country are done by peers rather than in a professional place," says Dennis Ranalli, a dentistry professor at the University of Pittsburgh School of Dental Medicine. "Kids are doing it to each other." Indeed, you can get a piercing starter kit for seventy-five dollars off the Internet; it doesn't include antiseptic, but it does have five consent forms.

"I have one patient right now who has self-pierced her eyelids with safety pins. There's inflammation and infection there," says Dr. Ranalli, who has studied mouth piercings. He's familiar with a wide range of piercing-related horror stories involving Ludwig's angina (bacterial infection of the mouth tissues so severe it threatens to cut off the airway) and bacterial endocarditis (an infection of the tissues of the heart). He says there has been one report of HIV transmission by piercing, a tongue piercing resulting in a hypertensive collapse, and another resulting in cephalic tetanus.

"These aren't just localized 'Oh, my tongue hurts' kinds of things," Dr. Ranalli says. "These could be serious, life-threatening problems. The medical profession is left treating the consequences of these things that are done for, quote, body art. So it's a problem." The irony for Dr. Ranalli is that "some of these kids won't go to the dentist because they're afraid. Meanwhile, you let somebody puncture your tongue with a large-gauge harpoon. It's strange."

The infection rate for piercings of the body other than of the lower earlobe can be as high as 50 percent, according to a study by the Oregon Department of Human Services.

81

Where You Live Matters

High levels of air pollution are a significant health risk. Your decision on where to live can be as important as your decision on how to live.

"The problem is that many environmental consequences, intended or not, are immediate. Change is happening faster than ever, and we can't always wait for the scientific proof. We think that if you can prevent a problem by taking precautionary action, you should do so, even if the evidence isn't all there," said Diane Takvorian, executive director of the San Diego–based Environmental Health Coalition. Diane's group urges the public to recognize pressing threats to health quickly to minimize the damage done.

For more than a decade, she said, local environmentalists had complained that a chrome-plating operation in the San Diego area was releasing dangerous amounts of toxic chemicals into the surrounding residential neighborhood. As a result, they said, children in the area experienced abnormally high levels of asthma and other ailments.

"Common sense tells you that if you spew a known carcinogen onto homes right next door, bad things will happen," Diane said.

Diane and others repeatedly asked for local or state officials to conduct scientific tests of the facility, but nothing happened for years. Finally, the San Diego County Air Pollution Control District arranged a monitoring program to measure airborne levels of chromium-6, a known carcinogen. Officials found dangerous amounts, she said, but the levels exceeded all established risk models, leaving the researchers unable to draw scientifically valid conclusions. It took another monitoring effort last year by the state before the facility was finally shut down.

"Everyone had a gut feeling this was not a good place," Diane said. "We tried hard to get the science to back that feeling up, but in the absence of hard data, you have to make a judgment.

"The state spent close to a million dollars," she adds, "and it took more than a decade to resolve this problem. If somebody had simply taken some precautionary measures earlier—relocating the company or buying pollution control equipment—we could have avoided all of this and the community would have been healthier earlier."

Stanford University researchers compared people living in cities with the highest and lowest levels of average daily air pollution. Those in the high pollution cities were 19 times more likely to need hospital care for respiratory conditions.

82

Electric Brushing Is Easier
but Not Much Different

Are electric toothbrushes and other automatic devices worth the expense? If you would not do a thorough job of brushing with your manual toothbrush, the answer is yes. If you would otherwise brush for as long and in the style recommended by your dentist, then the answer is no.

Dr. Mark Harris has a message for his dental patients and for everyone else: "Brushing your teeth is not like scrubbing your floors."

He explains, "Some people think that a stiff, hard brush applied with a vengeance is an effective approach, but plaque doesn't have to be scrubbed off, just reached, and a soft brush does less damage. Some older people show evidence of grooves from hard brushing."

The most effective brushing is gentle and practiced often. "You would do yourself much more good brushing well after every meal than giving yourself the top-of-the-line automatic toothbrush and using it once a day."

On the other hand, Dr. Harris says, "Some people are simply not going to listen to directions. And just as they might scrub too hard and take the finish off their car, they can brush too hard and damage their teeth and gums. For those people, I recommend taking your car to a car wash and giving your teeth an automatic toothbrush."

But preventing cavities and gum disease depends on all areas of the teeth getting cleaned. "Whatever toothbrush you use, you should make sure it enables you to reach everywhere in your mouth. If you can't comfortably brush your back teeth, you need a toothbrush that can help you."

The Mayo Clinic found that properly brushing and flossing manually is just as effective as using electric products. However, people who have difficulty using manual products, such as arthritis sufferers, benefited from use of electric toothbrushes and electric flossing devices.

83

Be Careful with Botox

Botox is everywhere in the headlines and news shows. The popular conception is that a quick and easy injection can take years off the appearance of your face. But Botox is a serious medical procedure that should not be considered without your doctor's input and should be administered only by a trusted physician.

The new rage—the Botox party—may seem like innocent fun for those who want to participate in this nonsurgical cosmetic procedure. But the chair of plastic surgery at the University of Texas Southwestern Medical Center at Dallas cautions that there can be unwanted consequences.

Dr. Rod Rohrich warns, "It is important for people who are considering attending these parties to check the credentials of the person who will be doing the procedure. Botox should be used only by a qualified, trained physician. This procedure is not like applying an antiwrinkle cream. Botox is a drug, and there is a potential for complications."

Dr. Rohrich explains, "When small doses of Botox are injected into the muscle, the serum works by blocking the signal that causes the muscle to contract. This is how Botox helps smooth out wrinkles around the eyes, forehead, and mouth. One treatment generally lasts from three to four months."

He adds, "Some people may not be good candidates for Botox. So it's important that each potential patient be evaluated individually and informed by a physician of the risks involved before having the procedure done."

Dr. Rohrich advises patients to be on the lookout for unscrupulous businesses that may dilute Botox and sell treatments for as low as $100. "If someone is quoting you an unreasonably low price, the serum may be watered down, and results will not last as long." He also warns against Botox parties where alcohol may be served. "Drinking and medical procedures don't mix."

According to the American Society of Plastic Surgeons, more than 1.6 million Botox procedures are performed each year, and the treatment has already become the most common nonsurgical cosmetic procedure done in the United States. Botox is made from a protein produced by a bacterium, *Clostridium botulinum,* and can cause drooping eyelids and asymmetry of facial features.

84

Pay Attention to Chronic Conditions

People can have a health condition for decades and not directly feel its effects. High blood pressure is considered by doctors to be a silent killer because a person can unknowingly have the condition for a very long time and then be completely debilitated by a heart attack or stroke. Just because you cannot see the effects right now does not mean a health condition should be ignored. Health is about your long-term well-being, not just about how you feel today.

Working for hospitals and health departments, Scott Evans has spent a career making sure people realize the importance of treating high blood pressure.

He speaks on the subject every chance he gets. "You may be among the one in four U.S. adults with high blood pressure. High blood pressure kills about fifty thousand Americans every year and contributes to the deaths of about five times as many."

Scott tells people that the longer it is left untreated, the more serious its complications can become. "There are no reliable symptoms, and nearly one-third of the estimated fifty million American people don't even know they have it. This is why high blood pressure is called the silent killer."

Scott adds, "Doctors don't know what causes high blood pressure except in a few rare cases. However, it is easily found and usually controllable. But the only way to tell if you have hypertension is to have a blood pressure check."

Scott explains that a normal level of blood pressure keeps blood circulating through the body. "And without circulating blood, vital organs such as the heart, kidneys, and brain can't get the oxygen and food they need to work. This lack of oxygen and food is what causes a heart attack, heart failure, kidney failure, stroke, blindness, and more. So it's important to know about blood pressure and how to keep it within a healthy level."

A University of South Carolina study found that up to 80 percent of people with high blood pressure were not receiving the recommended care for the condition, which effectively doubled their susceptibility to stroke, heart attack, and heart failure.

85

Weigh the Benefits of Alcohol Against the Risks

The positive effects of alcohol consumption on health have been documented in several high-profile studies. Light drinking has been linked to a reduced risk of heart disease. Moderate consumption of wine on a regular basis has been linked to lower cholesterol. Indeed, moderate consumption of alcohol has been linked to a longer overall life. However, each of these studies finds the positive effects of alcohol present only in a narrow range of consumption habits. Drinking too much overall, drinking too frequently, and drinking too much in one sitting are all habits that negate any positive effect of the alcohol.

Mark knows firsthand that alcohol can devastate a family. He is the director of a dependency clinic, but his own daughter died after a night of binge drinking.

Mark has spent his three-decade career trying to understand better the use and abuse of alcohol. While he has seen much progress since he began his career, Mark still feels that alcoholism is the poor stepchild of the health care field.

"People and governments do not understand the magnitude of the effect of alcoholism on the criminal justice and health care systems," he said. "The stigma still exists. Alcohol treatment is still restricted, and most people have limited benefit packages even when they seek treatment. The media and the advertising industry still glamorize drinking, and alcohol companies spend millions to attract new drinkers."

While he knows that health benefits have been associated with moderate alcohol consumption, he argues, "If alcohol were just invented today, no pharmaceutical company would try to sell it for its health benefits. No doctor would prescribe it. Nobody would take alcohol as a medicine with all its potential side effects."

Mark is all too familiar with the statistics. "One-quarter of all emergency room admissions, one-third of all suicides, and more than half of all homicides and incidents of domestic violence are alcohol related. Heavy drinking contributes to illness in each of the top three causes of death—heart disease, cancer, and stroke. Almost half of all traffic fatalities are alcohol related. More than half of the people who die in fires have blood alcohol levels indicating intoxication."

Mark adds, "Be grateful if alcohol doesn't hurt you, but I can't see anybody counting on alcohol actually helping them."

Drinking heavily does not show the same positive health benefits as light or moderate drinking, according to researchers at the State University of New York at Buffalo.

86

Regular Vitamins Do the Job

When it comes to vitamins, the recommended daily allowance is the amount you need every twenty-four hours. You don't need one-twenty-fourth that amount every hour or one-fourth that amount every six hours. Time-released vitamins are unnecessary.

Take nutritionist Nancy Reddick with you on a trip to the store, and you will be in for a rude awakening when you walk down the vitamin and supplements aisle.

"It's really like the Wild West in that aisle. Anything goes. Most of these products are not regulated, and they can make any claim they want."

Nancy explains, "They have products you don't need, products you don't need in that quantity, products with fancy features. And with supplements, it seems that advertising is open to the seller's creativity."

Nancy asks consumers to inform themselves before heading down the vitamin aisle. "If your diet does not contain sufficient vitamins and minerals, the best thing to do is change your diet. But if you are not going to do that, choose the vitamin that meets your needs given your age, sex, and diet. Don't let yourself get distracted by the bells and whistles. Buy only what you need."

When choosing a multivitamin, you don't have to waste extra money on time-release vitamins; regular multi-vitamins do just as well, according to a study at Tufts University.

87

Hug for Health

The small acts that comfort us and show us our connection to other people are not trivial. A hug is a means of giving and receiving affection—as well as a significant source of stress relief and comfort to our bodies.

"You say you're an M.D. prescribing hugs, and people will look at you funny," Dr. Laura Johnson says. "'Shouldn't you prescribe real medicines?' is what they're thinking."

Dr. Johnson explains, "People imagine the body is much more like a machine than it really is. They think that fixing a person should be like fixing a machine. Just put the right parts in, and there you go. The difference is, a machine doesn't have emotions. It doesn't care how you feel about it when you put in a new part. People do care, though. You can't have a purely functional approach to healing when people are not purely functional items."

Dr. Johnson has studied the effects of personal contact on hospital patients, including the amount of time family members and nurses spend with a patient. "The evidence is overwhelming. Everybody needs a daily dose of attention and a daily dose of touch for their emotional well-being. It is as important as diet and exercise."

A brief hug with a loved one reduced the effects of stress on blood pressure and heart rate by half, according to a study at the University of North Carolina.

88

Exercise for Your Mind

Regular exercise, starting with something as easy as a daily walk, benefits not only physical but also mental health. The functioning and efficiency of the brain have been shown to improve with exercise.

The children start running as soon as they enter the gymnasium. They warm up, sprint, and hold scooter races. Their physical education teacher, Nick Cestaro, encourages them to push themselves.

"I see the energy there. That's the way to let it out," he says. The children, a group of twenty-five who attend East Syracuse Elementary School, participate in a before-school program for youths who have a hard time staying focused in class.

The program is offered in addition to a regular physical education class during the school day. The before-school program aims to provide an extra release for the children, and it seems to be working. Cestaro and first-grade teacher Beth Crump say the extra activity helps pupils focus once they get in the classroom. Other teachers report seeing less fidgeting and fewer active behaviors and more self-control and focus.

One parent of a child in the program says it has helped improve his son's test scores by two grade levels. "This helped him out so much," the father said. "Now he's coming home and doing his homework. It kicks his energy down a little bit. He's so excited for early-morning gym class. His gym teacher is his idol."

Cestaro says, "The goals are short-term. If they can get a few more hours of focus, then we've succeeded. They come back happy every day because it's exciting and it's fun. It's natural, and it's good for you."

In a University of Illinois study, sedentary men and women were tested on their ability to plan, establish schedules, make and remember choices, and adapt to changing circumstances. Half were then assigned to a daily walking program, while the other half were not. When they were retested six months later, the walkers showed a 25 percent improvement. The nonwalkers made little mental progress.

89

Don't Let the Holidays Ruin Your Health

The holidays combine two major threats to our health in a short period of time. One is the availability of high-fat food in nearly limitless quantities. The second is the considerable stress that many of us feel because of high expectations or familial personality conflicts. This stress, in turn, leads many to consume even more food. Strive for a holiday that can be enjoyed, not one that is perfect. Let yourself eat more than you might normally but not to the point of gorging yourself. Nutritionists advise that to help you curtail your appetite during the holiday season, you consider drinking water before meals, eat light snacks one or two hours before meals, and walk as much as you can before and after eating big holiday meals.

Monica has spent almost every Thanksgiving of her married life with her husband's side of the family in Ohio. But this year the couple has declined the invitation. With their son approaching three, she says, they want to stay home and start creating their own holiday traditions.

What they've started, though, is a family drama with Monica as wicked daughter-in-law waging war against a family tradition. "I'm clearly the bad guy here," Monica says. "My mother-in-law sees this as a snub. I'm pulling her son out of the bosom of the family."

Monica says she and her husband feel bad about the conflict their decision to stay home has created. "This is hard for us," she says. "My husband feels trapped. He doesn't want to hurt his mother and brother, but at the same time he wants us to be together here."

To try and satisfy her husband's family and her own family, including her six siblings, Monica schedules as many visits as possible during the period between Thanksgiving and New Year's. "Unfortunately, there are two things there's never any shortage of: stress and food. We only get to see people briefly, which makes them unhappy. But even if we're coming for an hour, everybody feels compelled to use that time to feed us. It's a compulsion: 'You're here, eat.' I wouldn't want that much food in the course of a year, let alone over a month and a half. But you either eat or you offend, it seems."

With every passing year the pounds come, and Monica works on a strategy to accommodate everyone without having to eat her way through three states. "There has to be a better way than this. Of course I have to learn to say no, but it's hard to do when you are trying to please as many people as possible."

The average American gains seven to ten pounds between Thanksgiving and New Year's Day, according to exercise physiologists at Pennsylvania State University. Surveys show that anxiety levels are 55 percent greater over the holidays than at any other time of the year, which encourages stress eating.

90

Stretch Out and Fly Right

Sitting cramped for a very long period of time in dry conditions can affect our circulation system and cause potentially dangerous blood clots. Taking an airplane ride almost inevitably puts us in this situation. When flying, you can reduce your risk of circulation problems by moving around the cabin for at least five minutes every hour, massaging your legs from foot to thigh every hour, taking an aspirin before the flight, and drinking water while on board.

After Michael's flight from New York arrived in Paris, he collapsed. Doctors said he suffered a blood clot, which produced a pulmonary embolism. A clot impedes the free flow of blood, preventing tissues from getting needed oxygen and nutrients. It becomes life threatening if it dislodges and travels to the pulmonary artery in the lungs, where it becomes a pulmonary embolism and can cause sudden death. When Michael's French doctor nonchalantly told him that such clots were common among people getting off long flights, Michael said he was shocked.

Since then he has been on a campaign to persuade airlines to alert passengers to the risk and advise them what to do if they have symptoms of deep-vein thrombosis or pulmonary embolism. Michael also launched a Web site on the topic.

Michael cites statistics showing that as many as 10 percent of travelers over age fifty suffer from blood clots after long-distance flights. Other studies have found high numbers of apparent blood clots in long-distance travelers—motorists as well as fliers.

Concerned, the World Health Organization has begun studying the problem. And some international airlines are now printing warnings on tickets or showing videos on the subject before takeoff. One comforting finding is that the clots usually dissolve without any intervention, suggesting that while clots may be widespread, for most people the health effects are probably minimal.

Researchers at the Saitama Medical School in Moroyama, Japan, found that common airplane conditions reduced blood flow by 5 percent but that those effects could be reversed with proper hydration and stretching.

91

The Most Treatment Is Not the Best Treatment

"Do everything you can, doctor!" It's a natural inclination, but it is not necessarily a productive one. Getting more treatments or seeing more doctors does not guarantee better health.

A growing body of research is leading many medical experts to ask whether more is really better when it comes to health care.

Some medical specialties and geographical areas are suffering from a glut of doctors and hospitals, these experts say. Supply seems to drive demand. More hospitals in an area mean many more days spent in hospitals with no discernible improvements in health. More medical specialists mean many more specialist visits and procedures.

"If there are twice as many physicians, patients will come in for twice as many visits," said Dr. John E. Wennberg of Dartmouth Medical School, where much of the new work is being done. "Over the course of a lifetime, what increased spending buys you is generally unpleasant interventions like intensive care units and feeding tubes," Dr. Wennberg said.

"If you want to predict the amount of medical use, all you have to know is the medical supply," says Dr. Donald M. Berwick, president of the Institute for Healthcare Improvement, a nonprofit group in Boston. "The evidence to my mind is so strong," Dr. Berwick adds. "More is not better, and it often is very, very much worse."

A Dartmouth Medical School study found that as much as one-third of all medical care does not improve the health of the patient. Patients receiving more care overall do not have either better survival rates or higher satisfaction with their care.

92

Recognize the Difference Between Caution and Fear

It is easy to fear the traumatic experiences we witness on television or read about in the newspaper. But we need to recognize the difference between the legitimate dangers to our lives and the disastrous but rare events that befall people. Too often media coverage fails to make a distinction between real threats to our safety, which we should react to, and terrible but unpredictable traumas that we cannot rationally avoid. Understand that some of the most awful and memorable tragedies you can think of are so memorable precisely because they are so rare.

When two students brought high-powered guns to Columbine High School in Colorado in April of 1999, wounding and killing their fellow students and teachers, "the nation became terrified that our schools were no longer safe, even though the facts show they are safer than ever," said Glenn Muschert of Purdue University.

"There is a higher probability that children will be killed in their home, die from drug abuse, get hit by lightning, or be the victim of a drunk driver than be killed in school. Our schools are relatively safe, but Columbine created fear and terror in Americans for their children at school."

Although schools are safe compared to other settings, the danger seems bigger because these tragedies touch us in a personal way through the media. "My research shows our reactions went beyond this particular event, its victims or consequences," Professor Muschert said. "Through the press reports we can see how this event, which took place in a Denver suburb, affected people just as though it happened in a school in their neighborhood."

Professor Muschert said the fear created by Columbine and incidents like it fuels a misperception of how violence affects the country's youth. Studying how journalists cover crimes involving high school students helps explain why the nation believes such violence is on the rise when it actually is not, he said. "Youth have been increasingly thought of as being violent or as victims," Professor Muschert said. "This perception, reflected by the coverage of the Columbine shootings, creates a culture of fear regardless of the reality."

According to researchers at the University of Kentucky, we tend to fear most the things that are least likely to happen to us.

93

Be Careful What You Ask For

The ads are everywhere on television and in newspapers and magazines. "Ask your doctor" about a new medicine, they tell us. The ads extol the ability of the new product to cure everything from the life threatening to the trivial. What happens when people do ask their doctors about the drug? More often than not they get prescribed that very medication. Instead of asking your doctor about specific drugs, you are better off asking about your condition and seeing if the doctor thinks medications are needed.

Television and print advertising for prescription medicines aimed directly at consumers is soaring in the United States. So is the average American's spending on drugs.

Critics see a connection. They say ads are persuading Americans to buy drugs they don't need and are driving up the costs of an overburdened health care system.

Nancy Chockley, president of the National Institute for Health Care Management, reported that the 50 most heavily advertised drugs accounted for almost half of the $21 billion increase in drug sales in the United States between 1999 and 2000. The 9,800 other drugs accounted for the other half.

As an example of what she says is a disturbing trend, Nancy points to the differences between over-the-counter and prescription arthritis medication. "Clinical research shows they have the same effects. The prescription version costs forty times as much. But after a round of advertising, it is the prescription version that is being prescribed by more doctors."

Chockley continues, "It's very hard for physicians to say no to these drugs. You want that drug, your doctor writes a prescription in two minutes, and you walk away happy. If a doctor tells a patient he doesn't need it, the patient thinks, 'Gosh, he doesn't think I'm in pain.' It takes a half hour for the doctor to explain, and the patient leaves unhappy." Chockley notes that most doctors admit they have prescribed drugs they would not ordinarily recommend because of patient requests.

The Food and Drug Administration found that when patients ask their doctors about a drug they've seen advertised, 69 percent of the time the doctor will prescribe the advertised medicine.

94

Make Health a Convenience

When making their health decisions, people tend to factor in all the costs to themselves, including time and ease of access. In decisions ranging from your daily schedule to choosing a place to live, make it easy for health to fit into all your plans.

Dennis is a veteran of the navy now living on the west coast of Florida. He saw the effects immediately when the Veterans Administration combined its health facilities with its benefits office in Bay Pines, Florida.

Dennis was a patient in the VA medial center and a client in the career counseling center of the benefits office. "When they were two separate operations, fifty miles apart, you would have to make a choice between going to one and going to the other. Now they are in the same place, so the checkup I might have skipped because it was too far out of my way is now next door to where I was going anyway.

"Before," Dennis continues, "some people felt like it was a conspiracy, like they were trying to make it tough for us to use these services. This kind of disproves that. It's going to be good for a lot of veterans."

The department also reorganized the way it responds to inquiries so veterans can immediately talk with someone familiar with their case rather than getting passed from person to person. "We are trying to make things as convenient as possible," Veterans Administration spokeswoman Margaret Macklin said, "because we've found our services are more valuable when they are easy to access."

A Duke University study found that people who lived close to a hospital were 15 percent more likely to choose therapies doctors recommended over therapies that required fewer hospital visits.

95

Don't Drown Yourself in Water

Water gets a lot of attention in health circles, and rightfully so. It is the healthiest drink and should be a significant part of your liquid intake. But there is no reason to consume water as if you're in a competition. The positive effects of regular water do not translate into super effects when you drink even more water. You do not need to force yourself to drink water.

Dr. Heinz Valtin of the Dartmouth Medical School has studied water and its effects. He says there is simply no evidence to back the popular notion that people should drink eight glasses of water a day.

Dr. Valtin, a kidney specialist and author of two widely used textbooks on the kidney and water balance, sought to find the origin of this notion and to examine the scientific evidence, if any, that might support it. He observes that we see the exhortation everywhere: from health writers, nutritionists, even physicians. Dr. Valtin doubts its validity. Indeed, he finds it "difficult to believe that evolution left us with a chronic water deficit that needs to be compensated by forcing a high fluid intake."

Still, the eight-glasses-a-day rule is a way of life for many. How did the notion start? Dr. Valtin thinks it may have begun when the Food and Nutrition Board of the National Research Council recommended approximately "one milliliter of water for each calorie of food," which would amount to roughly two to two and a half quarts per day. Although in its next sentence the board stated, "Most of this quantity is contained in prepared foods," that last sentence may have been missed so that the recommendation was erroneously interpreted to specify how much water one should drink each day.

Despite the dearth of compelling evidence, then, what's the harm? "The fact is that, potentially, there is harm even in water. Too much can overload the kidneys," explains Dr. Valtin.

A Pennsylvania State University study found that typical foods consumed on a daily basis provide as much as 100 percent of the water consumption experts advise.

96

Health Is About Life

We see stories on the news about the latest pill, the latest treatment, the latest and most expensive remedy for whatever ails us. The health story we don't hear is that the route to a healthy life is not found in doctors' offices or hospitals. It is found in our home and in our daily life. Enjoying your life and the people around you will contribute to your health and reduce the effects of aging.

For Beth, nearly twenty years of dieting seemed nearly at an end. Two years ago she saw an ad for a prescription weight-loss drug that blocks fat absorption in the digestive system. She discussed it with her family doctor, who prescribed a month's supply.

Soon Beth learned the drug had an unpleasant side effect: sudden-onset diarrhea.

The drug is supposed to encourage dieters to stick to a low-fat diet because it makes excess fat in food leave the body through bowel movements. But even though Beth wasn't eating a high-fat diet, half an hour after eating, she'd have to be "close to a bathroom," she said.

The more she thought about it, though, the more she came to have doubts about the whole concept. "You can't be on a drug forever," she said. "The weight will come back. You go back to old habits that put on the weight in the first place."

Beth concluded, "If you don't change your life, there's simply no point to quick fixes." After going off the medication, Beth focused on reducing her daily calorie intake and walking every day.

She says she is relieved to be focusing on a healthy lifestyle instead of just losing pounds. "I try to eat healthier, get more exercise, and not be hard on myself if the scale doesn't go down as fast as I want," she said. "It's easier when I lean more on my friends and family and try to better appreciate everything in my life. And now I do feel better about myself, and I'm not always looking out for the nearest bathroom."

People who described their home lives as satisfying were 24 percent more likely to live beyond normal life expectancy, according to a University of California, Los Angeles, study.

97

Having a Pet Is Healthy

Few things in life are inherently sources of calm and good cheer. One of those sources is a family pet. Pets give us unconditional love and a steady positive form of responsibility, and they offer us comfort regardless of what else might be going on in our lives. As a result, we are actually healthier when we live with pets.

Wendy has shared her life with dogs for as long as she can remember. "When you come home from work after a long, hard day, who is the first family member to greet you at the door? In my house that would be Arthur, our Irish setter. He jumps up and down on his big feet and spins in circles. He barks. He looks at us with loving eyes that indicate that by merely walking through the front door, we have made him the happiest dog in the world," Wendy says.

While she thought of her dog as a source of love, she never thought about him as a source of health. Then a friend of hers was "prescribed" a dog as part of her treatment for cancer.

Wendy read up on the subjects of pets and health. "Ninety-seven percent of pet owners in a survey reported that their pet makes them smile at least once a day. Seventy-six percent believe their pet eases their stress level. People who live with dogs even go to the doctor less often than people who do not."

While she has always loved and appreciated her Irish setter, she feels even more indebted to him. "We used to think of him as a watchdog for the house, but he's also a watchdog for our health."

Pet owners are 15 percent less likely to suffer from high blood pressure than people who don't own pets, according to researchers at the State University of New York at Buffalo.

98

Vegetables Will Taste Better in the Future

Here's a comforting thought for those who find it difficult to eat right: vegetables will taste better to you in the future. How do we know that? It's not a time machine or some kind of science fiction prediction. Instead, we know that taste buds change with age and that as we get older the taste of vegetables becomes more appealing.

"Many people don't like to eat vegetables, and from the point of view of plants, the feeling is mutual," says Dr. Adam Drewnowski, director of the University of Washington Nutritional Sciences Program. He recently completed research that shows our demand for good taste is at odds with our need for good nutrition.

"Plants protect themselves against being eaten by secreting bitter-tasting toxins. In small amounts, the phenols, flavonoids, isoflavones, and other chemicals are proving to be good for us."

Our dislike of bitter flavors is natural. Humans and other animals associate bitter and sour taste with spoiled or poisonous food. For years, manufacturers have removed these unfavorable flavors through selective breeding and food processing, but that sacrifices some nutritional value.

The trick is to make bitter but healthy foods more palatable through preparation, says Dr. Drewnowski. His suggestion: take a cue from Mediterranean chefs, who typically season bitter vegetables with a dash of salt and olive oil. The oil helps blunt the bitter taste and adds its own heart-healthy benefits.

Even more important, Dr. Drewnowski notes, our sensitivity to bitterness declines with age. "Odds are, you will like vegetables more as you get older."

According to a University of Washington study, our taste buds change with age, including a declining sensitivity to bitterness. This makes many healthy foods more appealing to us as we get older. Eight in ten older people reported a growing preference for green vegetables, whole-grain foods, and bitter fruits like grapefruits and lemons.

99

Follow Through for Better Health

People who do what they say they are going to do tend to be healthier than people who don't follow through. Develop a long-standing habit of reliability, and benefits for your health and your life will follow.

Psychology professor Alan Christensen of the University of Iowa has found that our attitudes and approaches to life matter to our health. "You will be better off if you're conscientious," he says.

"Conscientiousness refers to diligence, a strong sense of personal control, and a willingness to take on personal challenges. In short, it is a commitment to follow the course you set yourself on without reluctance."

Professor Christensen says that it may be as important to think about how patients approach the world and themselves as it is to consider their physical state. "We all know people who tend toward anxiety or inaction. Typically we just think, 'Oh, that's just how they are,' and don't pay attention to it as a potentially important factor in their physical health. But we should be paying attention because these traits could be shortening their lives."

Although we don't usually think of such lifelong enduring traits as being easy to change, Professor Christensen said that there is reason to believe individuals can alter their degree of conscientiousness. Moreover, doctors should be able to use information about how their patients' personalities may be putting them at risk to judge how closely they need to be monitored and how aggressively to treat them.

In a study of those suffering from a chronic illness, University of Iowa researchers found that those who tended to be highly conscientious, goal directed, and dependable were 36 percent less likely to die prematurely.

100

Complete Health Is Rare

An interest in health is a very useful thing. An obsession with health is, however, a dangerous thing. Having a few health concerns at any given moment is normal. The best approach to health is to minimize health problems, not eliminate them.

Corbin Lacina of the Minnesota Vikings tells his teammates to cheer up when they step onto the field for the first day of training camp, which is a month-long series of practices preceding the regular season. "Just remember how you feel right now. Because it's the best you're going to feel for six months."

Players agree that the toughest part of their job is the day after a game. "At times it can be unbearable," said teammate Byron Chamberlain. "You wake up Monday morning, and the first step out of the bed is one of the most painful things in the world. I've had times when I literally think, 'How do I do this?'" Byron said. "And it might be, say, week three or four, and you're thinking, 'I've got twelve more games to go, how do I get through this?'"

Vikings receiver Chris Walsh said, "They say a game is like having twenty or thirty car crashes."

The majority of the Vikings don't get badly injured, however. Most won't be listed on the team's weekly injury report. But that doesn't mean they're not practicing and playing with considerable discomfort.

In the National Football League, the concept of feeling perfect is seldom imagined. Said Vikings coach Mike Tice, "If you are completely healthy that means you're not playing.

"You just become desensitized to it. You just have to realize that's just the way you feel all the time during the season," Corbin added. But there is one sure way to ease everybody's pain. And that's winning. "Of course," Byron said, "everything is a little better when you win. And everything hurts a little worse when you lose."

Emory University researchers found that less than 19 percent of Americans could be classified as completely healthy (with high levels of physical and mental health and low levels of illness) at any given moment.

Sources

"100 Million Americans Live with Aching Backs." 2002. *Spine.*

"Age Affects Taste of Vegetables." 2003. University of Washington, Seattle, Washington.

"Air Pollution Linked to Increased Medical Care and Costs for Elderly." 2002. *Health Affairs.*

"Airport Noise Impairs Long-Term Memory and Reading." 2002. *Psychological Science.*

"Allergies Interfere with Life." 2002. American College of Allergy, Asthma, and Immunology, Arlington Heights, Illinois.

"An Aspirin a Day to Keep Cancer Away?" 2002. Mayo Clinic, Rochester, Minnesota.

"Breathing and Blood Flow." 2003. Harvard University, Cambridge, Massachusetts.

"Caffeine-Signaling Activity in Brain Function." 2002. *Nature.*

"Can Forgiveness Make the Immune System Stronger?" 2002. University of Maryland, College Park, Maryland.

"Checklist of Claims May Signal Trouble on Internet Cancer-Treatment Sites." 2003. *Psychosomatics.*

"Choosing the Right Drink for Fluid Replacement." 2002. Geisinger-Wyoming Valley Human Motion Institute, Wilkes-Barre, Pennsylvania.

"Columbine News Coverage Misled Nation Down Fearful Road." 2003. Purdue University, West Lafayette, Indiana.

"Common Painkiller May Hinder Aspirin's Effects." 2002. Mayo Clinic, Rochester, Minnesota.

"Commonly Used Medicines May Delay or Prevent Alzheimer's Disease." 2002. *Neurology.*

"Connection Between Personality, Death Among Chronically Ill." 2002. *Health Psychology.*

"Distance to Treatment Center and Mastectomy vs. Lumpectomy." 2003. *International Journal of Radiation Oncology, Biology, and Physics.*

"Effect of Dogs and Cats on Health." 2002. *Journal of the American Medical Association.*

"Effects of Contact on Stress." 2003. University of North Carolina, Chapel Hill, North Carolina.

"Effects of Sleep Deficiency." 2003. National Sleep Foundation, Washington, DC.

"Effects of Time-Release Vitamins." 2003. Tufts University, Boston, Massachusetts.

"Effects on Cognitive Ability of Sedentary Lifestyle." 2003. University of Illinois, Champaign-Urbana, Illinois.

"Exposing Anti-Aging Propaganda." 2003. University of Illinois, Chicago, Illinois.

"Fertility and the Mountain Biker." 2002. University Hospital, Innsbruck, Austria.

"Fire Deaths Without Smoke Detectors." 2002. Centers for Disease Control, Atlanta, Georgia.

"Fit Seniors Better Able to React When Quick Thinking Needed." 2002. *American College of Sports Medicine.*

"Fitness Can Be Free." 2002. University of Richmond, Richmond, Virginia.

"Foods Rich in Folate May Reduce Risk of Stroke." 2002. *Stroke: Journal of the American Heart Association.*

"Fourth of July Safety Advice." 2002. American Academy of Orthopaedic Surgeons, Rosemont, Illinois.

"Ginkgo Fails to Aid Memory in Double-Blind Study." 2002. *Journal of the American Medical Association.*

"Half of Heart Attack Patients Drive to Hospital." 2002. *Circulation: Journal of the American Heart Association.*

"Health and Nutritional Differences Between Organic Foods and Traditionally Grown Foods." 2003. University of Michigan, Ann Arbor, Michigan.

"Health Benefits of Moderate Drinking May Not Apply to African-Americans." 2003. *Alcoholism: Clinical and Experimental Research.*

"High Hostility May Predict Heart Disease More than Other Risk Factors." 2002. *Health Psychology.*

"Home Injury Found to Be a Major Cause of Deaths." 2002. University of North Carolina, Chapel Hill, North Carolina.

"Household Mold Scares: Small Amounts Not a Big Health Concern." 2003. Mayo Clinic, Rochester, Minnesota.

"Ideal Body Images." 2002. U.S. Department of Health and Human Services, Washington, DC.

"Insect Repellent Study Reveals Widely Varied Protection Levels." 2002. *New England Journal of Medicine.*

"Involuntary Smoke Exposure Affects Asthma Severity Among Children." 2002. *Chest.*

"Jogging Every Day May Keep Alzheimer's Away." 2002. *Trends in Neurosciences.*

"Journal Writing Can Alleviate Illnesses." 1999. *Journal of the American Medical Association.*

"Large Doses of Vitamins and Minerals May Put Prostate Cancer Patients at Risk." 2002. *International Journal of Radiation Oncology, Biology, and Physics.*

"Lawn Mower Safety Could Save Life and Limb This Summer." 2003. University of Michigan, Ann Arbor, Michigan.

"Link Between Grape Juice Consumption and Lowered Risk of Heart Trouble." 2003. *Journal of the American Heart Association.*

"Little 'Weekend Effect' Related to Intensive Care Admissions." 2002. *Medical Care.*

"Lonely People Face Higher Risk of Heart Disease." 2002. *Psychosomatic Medicine.*

"Low Vitamin C Intake Linked with Stroke Risk." 2002. *Stroke: Journal of the American Heart Association.*

"Majority of U.S. Adults Have Some Health Problems." 2002. *American Journal of Health Promotion.*

"Managing Fatigue." 2002. Mayo Clinic, Rochester, Minnesota.

"Many Young Americans Risk Skin Cancer from Annual Sunburns." 2002. *American Journal of Preventive Medicine.*

"Medical Residents Fail to Perform Self Exams." 2003. Medical College of Georgia, Augusta, Georgia.

"Meditation Effects on Immune System." 2003. University of Wisconsin, Madison, Wisconsin.

415

"Memory Isn't Lost—Just out of Sync." 2002. University of Arkansas, Fayetteville, Arkansas.

"More Exercise, Less Smoking May Extend, Enhance Life Even at Advanced Age." 2002. *Psychosomatic Medicine.*

"More Health Care Doesn't Equal Better Health Care." 2003. *Annals of Internal Medicine.*

"Most Golf 'Yippers' Perceive Symptoms as Physical, not Psychological." 2003. Mayo Clinic, Rochester, Minnesota.

"Mothers Who Lose Weight After the Birth of Their First Child Have a 'Can Do' Attitude." 2001. *Journal of the American Dietetic Association.*

"Nearness of Supermarkets Boosts People's Intake of Nutritious Fruits, Vegetables." 2002. *American Journal of Public Health.*

"New Food-Addiction Link Found." 2002. *Synapse.*

"One-on-One with Pharmacists Gives Patients Medication Advantage." 2002. *American Journal of Health-System Pharmacy.*

"Only 5 to 10 Percent of Cancers Are Inherited." 2002. Mayo Clinic, Rochester, Minnesota.

"Physicians Honor Patient Requests for Advertised Drugs." 2002. Food and Drug Administration, Washington, DC.

"Piercing Your Ears? Stick to the Lobes." 2002. Presented at the Annual Meeting of the Infectious Diseases Society of America.

"Poor Sleep Linked to Earlier Death in Older Adults." 2003. *Psychosomatic Medicine.*

"Preventing Food-Borne Illness When Cooking and Eating Outdoors." 2002. Cedars-Sinai Medical Center, Los Angeles, California.

"Regular Soap Safer than Antibacterial Soap." 1999. Hackensack University Medical Center, Hackensack, New Jersey.

"Religiosity Effect on Mental Health." 2003. Columbia University, New York, New York.

"Researchers Link Red Wine to 'Good Cholesterol.'" 2002. *Alcoholism: Clinical and Experimental Research.*

"Sense of Control Eases Physical Toll of Stressful Situation." 2002. *Psychophysiology.*

"Sex Discrimination in Your Medicine Cabinet." 2002. Society for Women's Health Research in Washington, DC.

"Sick-Building Syndrome." 2001. World Health Organization, Geneva Switzerland.

"Skip the Elevator." 2000. Centers for Disease Control, Atlanta, Georgia.

"Smoking Outside Still Causes Secondhand Smoke Exposure to Children." 2002. Columbus Children's Hospital, Columbus, Ohio.

"Snacking Linked to Lower Cholesterol." 2002. Mayo Clinic, Rochester, Minnesota.

"Spouses Often Mirror Each Others' Health." 2002. *Social Science and Medicine.*

"Strong Religion Helps Cardiac Rehab Patients in Recovery." 2002. *Journal of Cardiopulmonary Rehabilitation.*

"Study Links Medicaid, Hypertension Risks." 2002. University of South Carolina, Columbia, South Carolina.

"Study Warns of Eating Meals in Front of TV." 2002. *Journal of Developmental and Behavioral Pediatrics.*

"Super-Hydration." 2002. *American Journal of Physiology.*

"Supportive Spouse, Family, Friends Contribute to 'Successful Aging.'" 2002. *Psychosomatic Medicine.*

"Teen Anxiety, Chances of Harmful Smoking and Eating Behavior Higher than Expected." 2002. *"Journal of the American Academy of Child and Adolescent Psychiatry.*

"Teens and Tanning: a Dangerous Combination." 2003. American Academy of Dermatology, New York, New York.

"Time to Debunk Cold-Season Myths." 2002. University of Texas Southwestern Medical Center, Dallas, Texas.

"Tobacco Smoke Linked to Reading, Math, Logic, and Reasoning Declines in Children." 2002. Cincinnati Children's Hospital, Cincinnati, Ohio.

"Toothbrush and Floss Compare Well to Electric Versions." 2002. Mayo Clinic, Rochester, Minnesota.

"Use Caution, Ask Questions Before Attending Botox Party." 2002. University of Texas Southwestern Medical Center, Dallas, Texas.

"When Traveling, Leave the Extra Baggage at Home." 2002. American Academy of Orthopaedic Surgeons, Rosemont, Illinois.

"Whitening May Cause Short-Term Tooth Sensitivity." 2002. *Journal of the American Dental Association.*

"Why Do the Elderly Fall?" 2002. Virginia Tech, Blacksburg, Virginia.

"Women's Shoes Increase Risk of Osteoarthritis." 2003. University of Virginia, Charlottesville, Virginia.

"Work and Marriage Influences Blood Pressure." 2002. Presented at the Annual Scientific Meeting of the American Society of Hypertension.

"Worksite Program to Stop Smoking Among Blue-Collar Workers Yields Notable Success." 2002. *Cancer Causes and Control.*

"Yoga May Be Prescription for Better Health." 2002. Florida State University, Tallahassee, Florida.